100 *of the best* SHOW TUNES *ever!*

This publication is not authorised for sale in the United States of America and/or Canada.

HLE

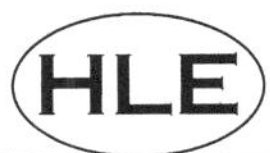

Exclusive Distributors:
Music Sales Limited
14-15 Berners Street, London W1T 3LJ, UK.

Order No. HLE90003056
ISBN 1-84609-589-1

Cover design by Chloë Alexander
Cover photos (*left to right*) – Front: Michael Le Poer Trench/Rex Features; YM/Keystone USA/Rex Features; Sinopix/Rex Features.
Back: Andrew Milligan/Rex Features; London Features International; Alastair Muir/Rex Features.
Printed in the USA

Your Guarantee of Quality
As publishers, we strive to produce every book to the highest commercial standards.
The book has been carefully designed to minimise awkward page turns and to make playing from it a real pleasure.
Throughout, the printing and binding have been planned to ensure a sturdy, attractive publication which should give years of enjoyment.
If your copy fails to meet our high standards, please inform us and we will gladly replace it.

www.musicsales.com

6 **All I Ask Of You** *The Phantom Of The Opera*

18 **All The Things You Are** *Very Warm For May*

11 **Any Dream Will Do** *Joseph And The Amazing Technicolor® Dreamcoat*

22 **As Long As He Needs Me** *Oliver!*

24 **Beauty And The Beast** *Beauty And The Beast*

28 **Being Alive** *Company*

36 **Bewitched** *Pal Joey*

33 **Big D** *The Most Happy Fella*

40 **Broadway Baby** *Follies*

46 **A Bushel And A Peck** *Guys And Dolls*

48 **Cabaret** *Cabaret*

52 **Can't Help Lovin' Dat Man** *Show Boat*

55 **Circle Of Life** *The Lion King*

60 **Climb Ev'ry Mountain** *The Sound Of Music*

63 **Dancing Queen** *Mamma Mia!*

68 **Day By Day** *Godspell*

71 **Do I Love You Because You're Beautiful?** *Cinderella*

74 **Don't Cry For Me Argentina** *Evita*

82 **Don't Cry Out Loud (We Don't Cry Out Loud)** *The Boy From Oz*

86 **Edelweiss** *The Sound Of Music*

96 **Falling In Love With Love** *The Boys From Syracuse*

89 **Follow Your Heart** *Urinetown*

104 **For Good** *Wicked*

116 **Getting To Know You** *The King And I*

120 **Glad To Be Unhappy** *On Your Toes*

122 **Hard Candy Christmas** *The Best Little Whorehouse In Texas*

126 **Hello, Young Lovers** *The King And I*

113 **I Believe In You** *How To Succeed In Business Without Really Trying*

132 **I Can Hear The Bells** *Hairspray*

144 **I Don't Know How To Love Him** *Jesus Christ Superstar*

148 **I Dreamed A Dream** *Les Misérables*

154 **I Enjoy Being A Girl** *Flower Drum Song*

162 **I'll Be Seeing You** *Right This Way*

166 **I'm Gonna Wash That Man Right Outa My Hair** *South Pacific*

172 **If I Loved You** *Carousel*

141 **If I Were A Bell** *Guys And Dolls*

176 **If I Were A Rich Man** *Fiddler On The Roof*

184 **The Impossible Dream (The Quest)** *Man Of La Mancha*

188 **It Might As Well Be Spring** *State Fair*

202 **The Joint Is Jumpin'** *Ain't Misbehavin'*

206 **June Is Bustin' Out All Over** *Carousel*

212 **Kiss Of The Spider Woman** *Kiss Of The Spider Woman*

222 **The Lady Is A Tramp** *Babes In Arms*

193 **The Last Night Of The World** *Miss Saigon*

226 **Little Girl Blue** *Jumbo*

231 **Look For The Silver Lining** *Sally*

234 **Love Changes Everything** *Aspects Of Love*

239 **Luck Be A Lady** *Guys And Dolls*

246 **Make Believe** *Show Boat*

258 **Mama, I'm A Big Girl Now** *Hairspray*

268 **Manhattan** *The Garrick Gaieties*

251 **Memory** *Cats*

272 **My Favorite Things** *The Sound Of Music*

276 **My Funny Valentine** *Babes In Arms*

281 **No Moon** *Titanic*

286 **Oh, What A Beautiful Mornin'** *Oklahoma!*

294 **Oklahoma** *Oklahoma!*

289 **Ol' Man River** *Show Boat*

300 **On My Own** *Les Misérables*

312 **Once In Love With Amy** *Where's Charley?*

305 **One Night In Bangkok** *Chess*

314 **People Will Say We're In Love** *Oklahoma!*

322 **Promises, Promises** *Promises, Promises*

319 **Put On A Happy Face** *Bye Bye Birdie*

326 **River In The Rain** *Big River*

330 **Seasons Of Love** *Rent*

338 **Seventy Six Trombones** *The Music Man*

348 **Shall We Dance?** *The King And I*

335 **Smoke Gets In Your Eyes** *Roberta*

352 **Some Enchanted Evening** *South Pacific*

362 **Somebody Loves Me** *George White's Scandals Of 1924*

366 **Someone Like You** *Jekyll & Hyde*

370 **The Song Is You** *Music In The Air*

374 **The Song That Goes Like This** *Monty Python's Spamalot*

357 **The Sound Of Music** *The Sound Of Music*

380 **Starlight Express** *Starlight Express*

386 **Sunrise, Sunset** *Fiddler On The Roof*

390 **Ten Cents A Dance** *Simple Simon*

400 **That Face** *The Producers*

406 **This Nearly Was Mine** *South Pacific*

412 **Thoroughly Modern Millie** *Thoroughly Modern Millie*

395 **'Til Him** *The Producers*

422 **Till There Was You** *The Music Man*

430 **Too Close For Comfort** *Mr. Wonderful*

425 **Unexpected Song** *Song And Dance*

436 **Unusual Way (In A Very Unusual Way)** *Nine*

444 **What I Did For Love** *A Chorus Line*

441 **What Kind Of Fool Am I?** *Stop The World – I Want To Get Off*

448 **When Did I Fall In Love** *Fiorello!*

454 **When Will Someone Hear?** *Martin Guerre*

458 **Where Is Love?** *Oliver!*

464 **Where Or When** *Babes In Arms*

461 **Who Can I Turn To (When Nobody Needs Me)** *The Roar Of The Greasepaint – The Smell Of The Crowd*

468 **Why Was I Born?** *Sweet Adeline*

472 **With A Song In My Heart** *Spring Is Here*

476 **With One Look** *Sunset Boulevard*

484 **Written In The Stars** *Aida*

481 **You'll Never Walk Alone** *Carousel*

494 **You're Nobody 'Til Somebody Loves You** *Contact*

490 **Younger Than Springtime** *South Pacific*

ALL I ASK OF YOU

from THE PHANTOM OF THE OPERA

Music by ANDREW LLOYD WEBBER
Lyrics by CHARLES HART
Additional Lyrics by RICHARD STILGOE

D♭maj7 G♭6/D♭ C♭ A♭/C
3fr
here, with you, be - side you, to guard you and to guide you.
D♭ B♭m7 E♭m7 A♭ D♭/F B♭m7
6fr 4fr
CHRISTINE:
Say you love me ev - ery wak - ing mo - ment, turn my head with talk of
E♭m7 E♭m7/A♭ D♭ B♭m7 E♭m7 A♭
6fr 6fr 6fr 4fr
sum - mer - time. Say you need me with you now and al - ways;
D♭/F G♭ D♭/A♭ E♭m/A♭ A♭6 E♭m7/A♭
4fr 6fr 3fr 6fr
prom - ise me that all you say is true, that's all I ask of
rit.

Db
RAOUL:
Dbmaj7
Gb6/Db
Let me be your shel - ter, let me be your light; you're safe, no one will find you your
you.
a tempo
mf
Cb
Ab/C
3fr
Db
CHRISTINE:
fears are far be - hind you. All I want is free - dom, a world with no more night; and
Dbmaj7
Gb6/Db
Cb
Ab/C
3fr
Db
Bbm7
RAOUL:
you, al - ways be - side me, to hold me and to hide me. Then say you'll share with me one
Ebm7
6fr
Ab
4fr
Db/F
Bbm7
Ebm7
6fr
G/Ab
3fr
Ab
4fr
Ab6
3fr
Ab7
4fr
love, one life - time; let me lead you from your sol - i - tude. _

D♭
B♭m7
E♭m7
A♭
D♭/F
G♭
Say you need me with you, here be - side you, an - y - where you go, let me go
D♭/A♭
E♭m7/A♭
A♭6
E♭m7/A♭
D♭
B♭m7
CHRISTINE:
too. Chris - tine, that's all I ask of you.
Say you'll share with me one
rit.
molto rit.
a tempo
f
E♭m7
A♭
D♭/F
B♭m7
E♭m7
A♭
A♭7
love, one life - time; say the word and I will fol - low you.
D♭
B♭m7
E♭m7
A♭
D♭/F
G♭
TOGETHER:
CHRISTINE:
8vb
Share each day with me, each night, each morn - ing. Say you love me!
RAOUL:
You know I
rit.

Db/Ab
Ebm7/Ab
Ab6
Ebm7/Ab
Db
Bbm7
RAOUL & CHRISTINE:
do. Love me, that's all I ask of you.
molto rit.
a tempo
Ebm7
Ab
Db/F
Bbm7
Ebm7
G/Ab
Ab
Ab6
Ab9
Db
Bbm7
Ebm7
Ab
Db/F
Gb
CHRISTINE & RAOUL:
An - y - where you go, let me go
f
ff largo
Db/Ab
Ebm7/Ab
Ab6
Ebm7/Ab
Db
RAOUL & CHRISTINE:
too; love me, that's all I ask of you.
mp
molto rit.

ANY DREAM WILL DO

from JOSEPH AND THE AMAZING TECHNICOLOR® DREAMCOAT

Music by ANDREW LLOYD WEBBER
Lyrics by TIM RICE

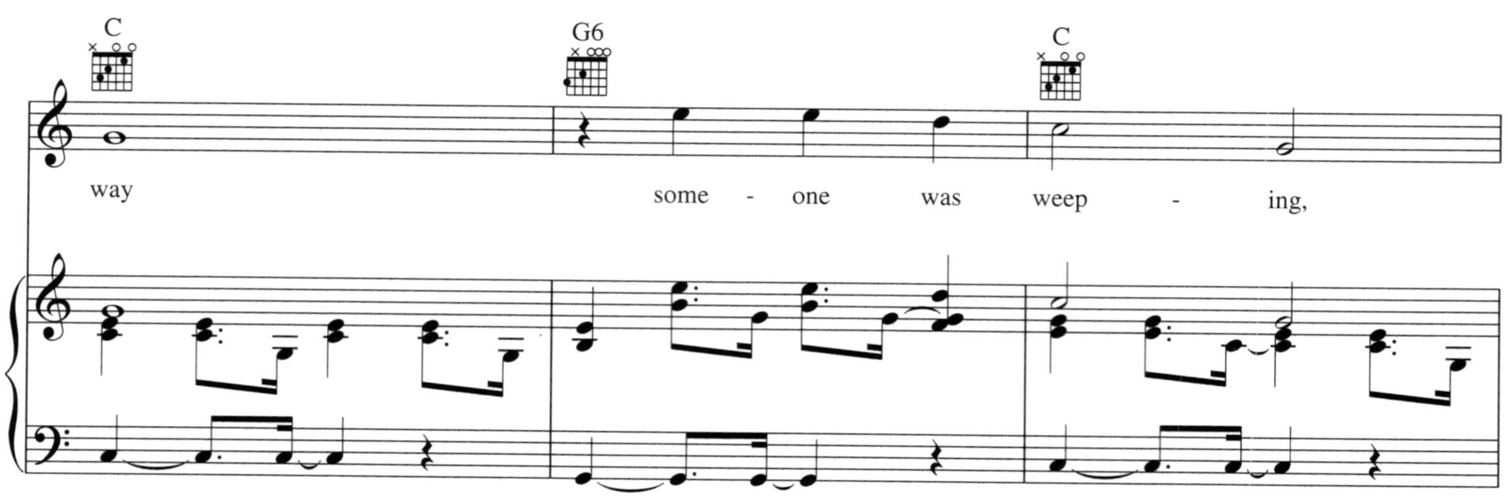
C
G6
C
way
some - one was weep - ing,

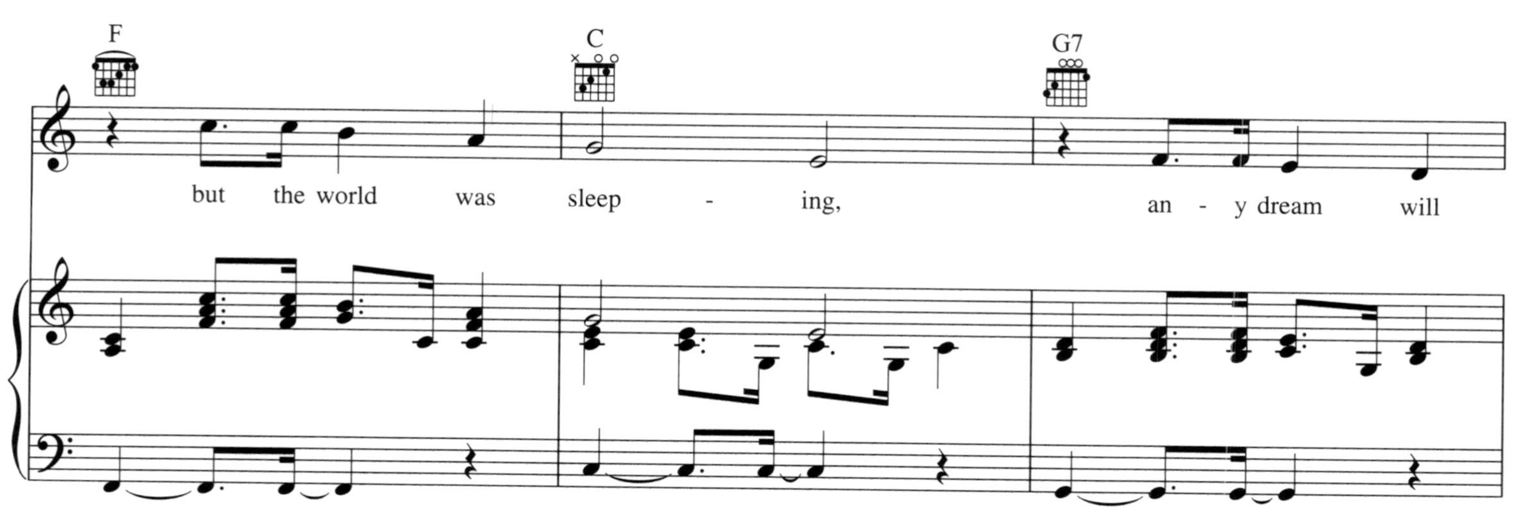
F
C
G7
but the world was sleep - ing,
an - y dream will

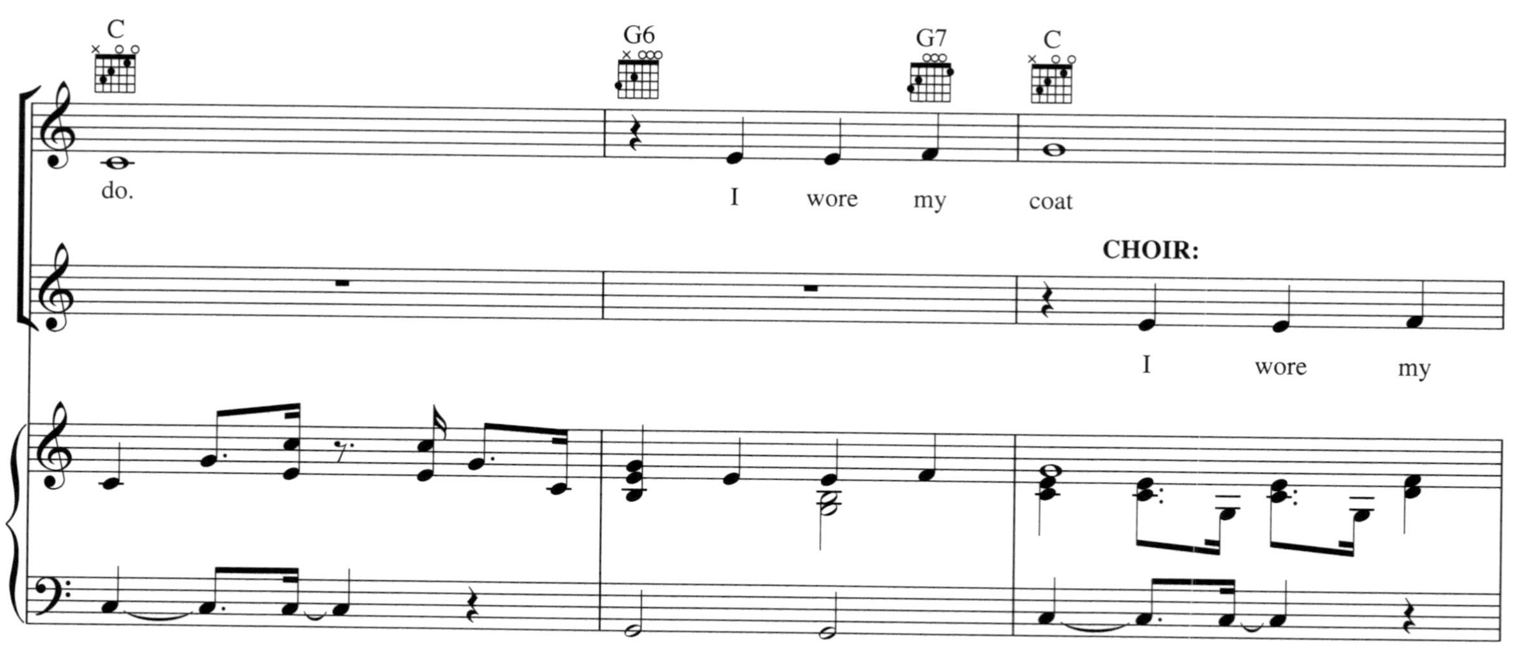
C
G6
G7
C
do.
I wore my coat
CHOIR:
I wore my

G6
C
F
with gold - en lin - ing, bright col - ours
coat, ah,
C
G7
C
shin - ing won - der - ful and new.
ah,
G6
G7
C
G6
And in the east the dawn was
and in the east,

C
F
C
break - ing,
and the world was
wak - ing,
ah,
ah,
G7
C
B♭/C
C7
JOSEPH:
an - y dream will
do.
A
F
F6
Fmaj7
F6
D7
D
crash of drums
a flash of light,
my gold - en coat flew

D9
4fr
C/G
G
C
G7
C/G
G7
C/G
G
Dm/G
G
D7/G
out of sight. The col - ours fad - ed in - to dark - ness, I was left a -
CHOIR:
The col - ours fad - ed in - to dark - ness, ah,
G
Dm7/G
G7
C
lone. May I re - turn,
ah, ah. May I re -
G6
C
F
to the be - gin - ning, the light is
turn, ah,

C G7 C

dim - ming and the dream is too,

ah.

G6 G7 C G6

the world and I, we are still

The world and I,

C F C

wait - ing, still hes - i - tat - ing

ah, ah.

G
C
Dm7/C
any dream will do,
Any dream, any dream will,
C
Dm7/C
C
any dream will do,
any dream, any dream will, do, any dream,
Dm7/C
C
Dm/G
C
any dream will do.
any dream will, any dream, any dream will do.
rall.

ALL THE THINGS YOU ARE

from VERY WARM FOR MAY

Lyrics by OSCAR HAMMERSTEIN II
Music by JEROME KERN

B7sus
B7
G
touch - ing your hand, my heart beats the fast - er. All that I want in
D7sus
D7
G
C7
B♭/C
C7
all of this world is you.
Fm7
B♭m7
E♭9
E♭7♭9
A♭maj7
You are the prom - ised kiss of spring - time that
D♭maj7
G7
G7♭5
Cmaj7
Bmaj7
Cmaj7
Cmaj9
C6
makes the lone - ly win - ter seem long.

Cm7
3fr
Fm7
B♭9
E7
E♭maj7
3fr
You are the breath - less hush of eve - ning that
A♭maj9
3fr
Am7♭5
D7
Gmaj9
Gm6/B♭
trem - bles on the brink of a love - ly song.
You are the
Am7
D9
4fr
Gmaj7
G6
Am7
Gmaj7
an - gel glow that lights a star,
the dear - est
F♯m7♭5
4fr
B7♭9
Emaj9
E6
C7♭9
C7
things I know are what you are.

Fm7
B♭m7
E♭9
E♭7♭9
A♭maj7
Some - day my hap - py arms will hold you, and
D♭maj7
G♭13
A♭(add9)/E♭
A♭/E♭
A♭dim7/E♭
some - day I'll know that mo - ment di - vine when
B♭m7/E♭
D♭maj7/E♭
E♭7♭9
1
A♭
B♭m7
C7♭9
all the things you are, are mine!
2
A♭
E
A♭maj7
mine!

AS LONG AS HE NEEDS ME

from the Broadway Musical OLIVER!

Words and Music by
LIONEL BART

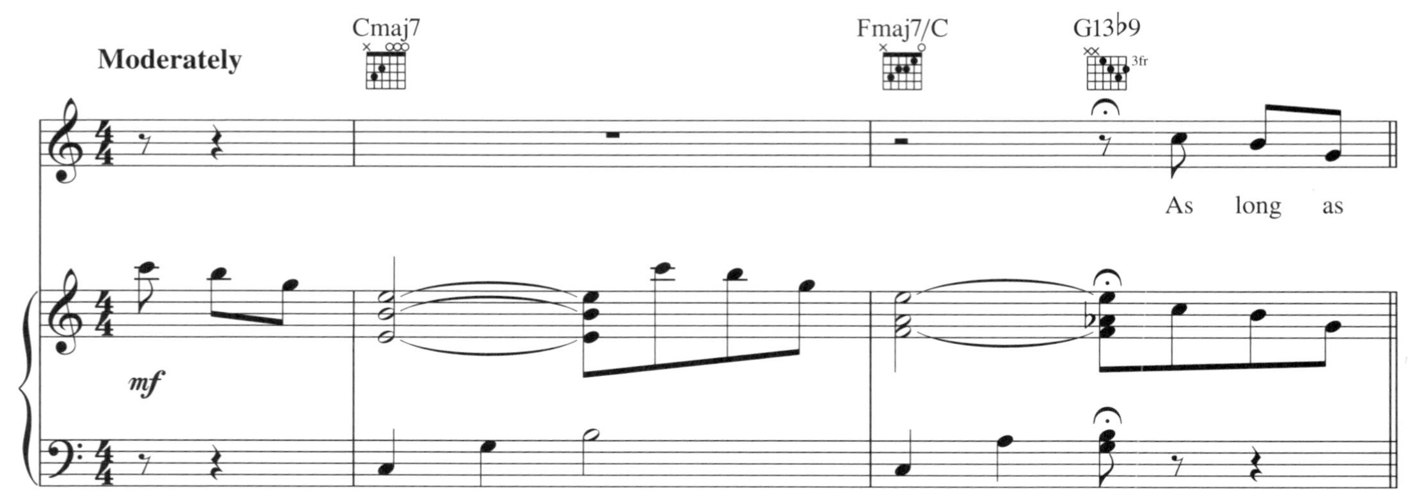

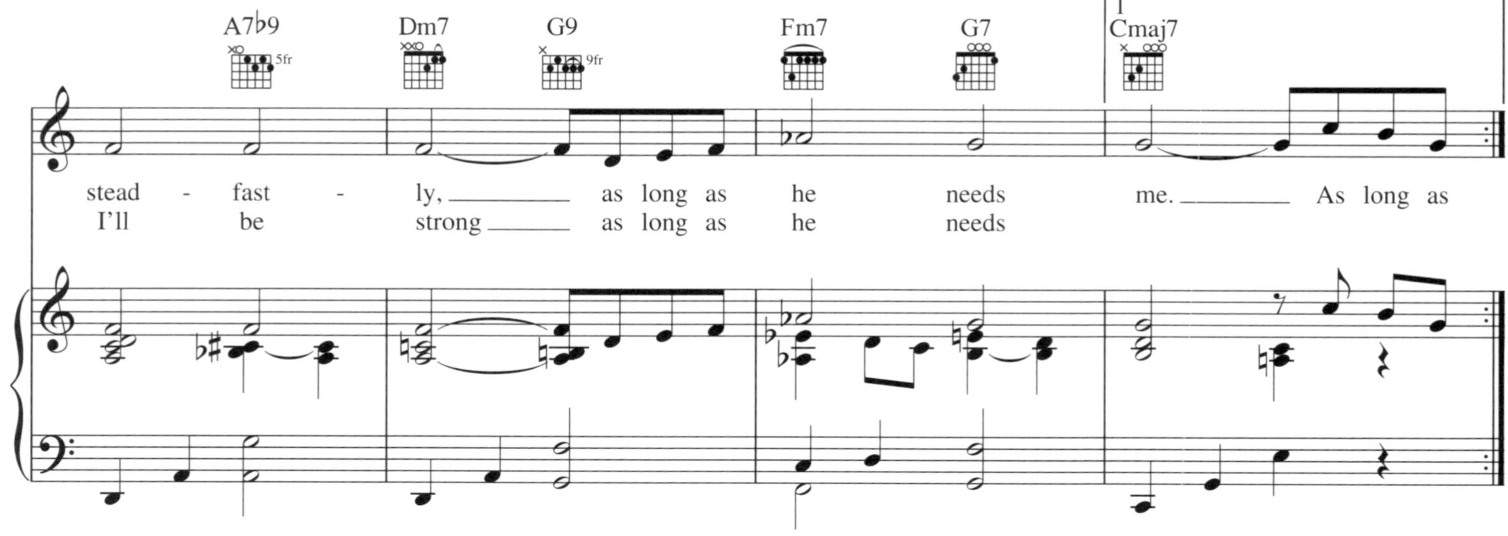

2
Cmaj7
C7
Fsus(add2)
G7
C
me. If you are lone - ly then you will know when some - one
Am
D9
4fr
Dm7
A♭13
4fr
G7
Cmaj7
Fmaj7/G
G13♭9
3fr
needs you you love them so. I won't be - tray his
Cmaj7
A7♭9
5fr
Dm7
trust, though peo - ple say I must. I've got to
A7♭9
5fr
Am7
D9
4fr
Dm7
A♭13
4fr
G7
C
stay true, just as long as he needs me.
f

BEAUTY AND THE BEAST

from Walt Disney's BEAUTY AND THE BEAST: THE BROADWAY MUSICAL

Lyrics by HOWARD ASHMAN
Music by ALAN MENKEN

G(add9)
G/A
A7sus
A7
D(add9)
2 fr
bends un - ex - pect - ed - ly. Just a lit - tle
A7sus
G/A
A7
D(add9)
2 fr
D
Am7
D7
change. Small, to say the least. Both a lit - tle
G(add9)
Gmaj7
F♯m7
Em7
G/A
A7
D
scared, nei - ther one pre - pared, Beau - ty and the Beast.
rall.
a tempo, tenderly
A7sus
D(add9)
2 fr
A7sus
F♯m
Ev - er just the same.

G(add9)
F♯m
G(add9)
F♯m7
Ev-er a sur-prise.
Ev-er as be-fore, ev-er just as
Bm
Bm7
2 fr
C
D
E
sure as the sun will rise.
Tale as old as
mf
B7sus
4 fr
B7
E
B7sus
4 fr
B7
time,
tune as old as song.
E
G♯m
4 fr
A
B7sus
4 fr
B7
Bit-ter-sweet and strange, find-ing you can change, learn-ing you were wrong.
dim.

E(add9)
B7sus
4 fr
B7
E(add9)
E
Bm7
2 fr
E7
Cer-tain as the sun
ris-ing in the East,
tale as old as
A
Amaj7
G♯m7
4 fr
F♯m7
B7sus
4 fr
B7
E
B/D♯
4 fr
C♯m
4 fr
E/B
time,
song as old as rhyme,
Beau-ty and the Beast.
Tale as old as
mp
dim.
p
A
Amaj7
G♯m7
4 fr
F♯m7
B7sus
4 fr
B7
E(add9)
time,
song as old as rhyme,
Beau - ty and the Beast.
8va
rall.
a tempo
Esus
B
B9
E(add9)
E
loco
8va
molto rall.
8vb

BEING ALIVE

from COMPANY

Words and Music by
STEPHEN SONDHEIM

Am7/D
Dm7/G
G13
3fr
Dm7/G
Fmaj7/G
3
ware of be - ing a - live, being a -
Dm7/G
G13
Dm7/G
G13
C6/9
live. Some-bod - y need me too
F/G
C6/9
G7♭9
much, some - bod - y know me too well,
C6/9
Am7
Fmaj9
some - bod - y pull me up short, and put me through hell, and give me sup -

Am7/D
Dm7/G
G13
Dm7/G
Fmaj7/G
port for be - ing a - live.
Make me a -
live,
make me a - live.
Make me con - fused,
mock me with
praise,
let me be used,
Ab/Bb
C
Cdim

Dm7/G
G13
Dm7/G
G7
vary my days,
but a-
Dm7/G
G13
G9
G9♯5
F/G
G13
lone is a-lone,
cresc.
F6/G
G9
G9♯5
Dm7/G
G13
Dm7/G
G13
not a-live.
f
C6/9
F/G
C6/9
G7♭9
Some-bod-y crowd me with love,
some-bod-y force me to care,

C6/9
Am7
Fmaj9
some-bod - y make me come through, I'll al-ways be there as fright-ened as
Am7/D
Dm7/G
G13
Fmaj7/G
you, to help us sur - vive
be-ing a -
Dm7/G
G13
live,
be-ing a - live,
be-ing a -
C
B♭/C
C11
live.
sfz
sfz

BIG D

from THE MOST HAPPY FELLA

By FRANK LOESSER

C+
Bb7
I mean Big D, lit - tle a, dou - ble l - a - s.
Eb6
Fm7
F#dim
Gm7-5
Bbm
Ebm7-5
Eb7
And that spells Dal - las, My
that spells Dal - las, Where
that spells Dal - las, Just
that spells Dal - las, I
Fm7
F#dim
Eb7
Ab
C7
Db7
C7
dar - lin', dar - lin' Dal - las, Don't it give you pleas - ure to con -
ev - 'ry home's a pal - ace 'Cause the set - tlers set - tle for no
dig a toe in Dal - las And there's oil all o - ver your ad -
mean it with no mal - ice But the rest of Tex - as looks a
F7
Bb7
Eb
Gm7-5
fess That you're from Big D? My, oh
less Hoo - ray for Big D, My, oh
dress Back home in Big D, My, oh
mess When you're from Big D, My, oh

C7
Bb7
yes. I mean Big D, lit - tle a, dou - ble l - a,
yes. I mean Big D, lit - tle a, dou - ble l - a,
yes. I mean Big D, lit - tle a, dou - ble l - a,
yes. I mean Big D, lit - tle a, dou - ble l - a,
Eb
Bb7
Big D, lit - tle a, dou - ble l - a, Big D, lit - tle
Big D, lit - tle a, dou - ble l - a, Big D, lit - tle
Big D, lit - tle a, dou - ble l - a, Big D, lit - tle
Big D, lit - tle a, dou - ble l - a, Big D, lit - tle
1,2,3
Eb6
Fm7
F#dim
Gm7-5
a, dou - ble l - a - s!
a, dou - ble l - a - s!
a, dou - ble l - a - s!
2. And
3. And
4. And
4
F9-5
Eb
a, dou - ble l - a - s!
f

BEWITCHED

from PAL JOEY

Words by LORENZ HART
Music by RICHARD RODGERS

* Standard lyric (in italics)
** Original show lyric.

Bm7
E7
Amaj7
F♯7♭9
Bm7
E7
Amaj7
Late - ly I've not slept a wink, Since this half - pint im - i - ta - tion
I've done pret - ty well, I think, But this half - pint im - i - ta - tion
Bm7
E13
Slowly
A
Put me on the blink. I'm wild a - gain, Be -
Put me on the blink. I'm wild a - gain! Be -
Seen a lot; I
Sweet a - gain, Pe -
rall.
p a tempo
E7sus/B
A/C♯
A+/C♯
D
Bdim7
guiled a - gain, A sim - per - ing, whim - per - ing child a - gain. Be -
guiled a - gain! A sim - per - ing, whim - per - ing child a - gain. Be -
mean a lot! But now I'm like sweet sev - en - teen a lot. Be -
tite a - gain, And on my pro - ver - bi - al seat a - gain. Be -
A/C♯
B7
E7
F♯7
Bm
Bm7
witched, both - ered and be - wil - dered am I.
witched, both - ered and be - wil - dered am I.
witched, both - ered and be - wil - dered am I.
witched, both - ered and be - wil - dered am I.

E7/B Bm7/E E7 A E7sus/B
Could - n't sleep And would - n't sleep, When
Could - n't sleep And would - n't sleep Un -
I'll sing to him Each spring to him And
What am I? Half shot am I. To
A/C♯ A+/C♯ D Bdim7 A/C♯ B7
love came and told me I should - n't sleep. Be - witched, both - ered and be -
til I could sleep where I should - n't sleep. Be - witched, both - ered and be -
wor - ship the trou - sers that cling to him. Be - witched, both - ered and be -
think that he loves me, So hot am I. Be - witched, both - ered and be -
E7 A7 D F♯7/C♯ F♯7 Bm6
wil - dered am I. Lost my heart, but what
wil - dered am I. Lost my heart, but what
wil - dered am I. When he talks he is
wil - dered am I. Though at first we said
F♯m(add9)
of it? He is cold, I a - gree,
of it? My mis - take, I a - gree.
seek - ing Words to get off his chest.
"No, sir." Now we're two lit - tle dears.

Bm7 E7 E7/B E7 E6 F7/E Bm7 E7
He can laugh, but I love it, Al-though the laugh's on me. I'll
He's a laugh, but I love it Be-cause the laugh's on me. A
Hor - i - zon - tal - ly speak - ing, He's at his ver - y best.
You might say we are clos - er Than Roe - buck is to Sears. I'm
A E7sus/B A/C♯ A+/C♯
sing to him, each spring to him, And long for the day when I'll
pill he is, But still he is All mine and I'll keep him un -
Vexed a - gain, Per - plexed a - gain, Thank God I can be o - ver -
dumb a - gain, And numb a - gain, A rich, read - y, ripe lit - tle
D Bdim7 A/C♯ B7 E7
[3rd vs.]
cling to him. Be - witched, both - ered and be - wil - dered am
til he is Be - witched, both - ered and be - wil - dered like
sexed a - gain. Be - witched, both - ered and be - wil - dered am
plum a - gain. Be - witched, both - ered and be - wil - dered am
[3rd vs.]
1, 2
A F♯m Bm E7
I. I'm
me.
I.
3
A D A(add9)
I.
I.
rall.

BROADWAY BABY

from FOLLIES

Words and Music by
STEPHEN SONDHEIM

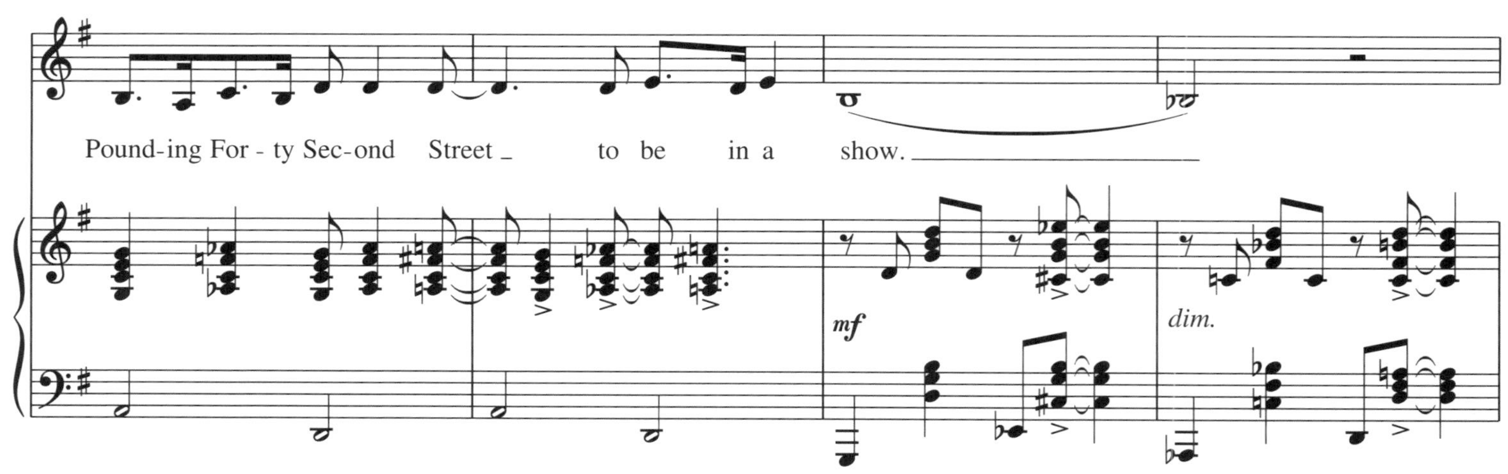

Broad-way Ba - by,
Learn-ing how to sing and dance,
Wait-ing for that one big chance to be in a show.
Gee, I'd like to be on some mar - quee, All twin - kling lights, a
spark to pierce the dark From Bat-t'ry Park to Wash - ing-ton Heights.
p
mf
3

Some day, may - be,
All my dreams will be re - paid.
Hell, I'd e - ven play the maid
to be in a
show!
Say, Mis - ter Pro - duc - er,
I'm talk - ing to you, sir.
I don't need a lot,

On - ly what I got,
Plus a tube of grease-paint and a fol-low spot! _ I'm a
Broad - way Ba - by, ___
Slav - ing at a five and ten, _
Dream-ing of the great day when _ I'll be in a
no swing beat
show! ___
8va
loco

Broad-way Ba-by,
Mak-ing rounds all af-ter - noon,
Eat-ing at a greas-y spoon to save on my dough.
Solid 4
At my ti-ny flat there's just my cat, a bed and a chair.
Still I'll stick it till I'm on a bill All o - ver Times Square.

Some day, may - be,
If I stick it long e - nough,
I can get to strut my stuff,
cresc.
Work - ing for a nice man like a Zieg - feld or a Weiss - man in a great big
f
Broad - way show!

A BUSHEL AND A PECK

from GUYS AND DOLLS

By FRANK LOESSER

C#dim
G
F
a - bout
you
'Cause
G
D7
G
D7
G
D7
I
love
you
A
Bu - shel And
A
Peck
y'
bet your pur - ty neck I
do
G
D7
G7
C
Doo - dle oo - dle oo - dle
Doo - dle oo - dle oo - dle
a
G
D7
1,2 G
D7
3 G
doo - dle oo - dle oo - dle
ooo.
8va

CABARET

from the Musical CABARET

Words by FRED EBB
Music by JOHN KANDER

Adim7
Gm
3fr
C9
cab - a - ret, old chum,
Fm7
B♭9
1
E♭
3fr
Fm7
B♭9
come to the cab - a - ret.
2
E♭
3fr
A♭m
4fr
ret. Come taste the wine, come hear the
E♭
3fr
Cm
3fr
Cm(maj7)
8fr
Cm7
3fr
F9
band, come blow the horn, start cel - e - brat - ing,

B♭7
E♭(add9)
B♭9
B♭9♯5
right this way, your table's waiting.
No use permitting some
Start by admitting from
E♭(add9)
B♭7♯5
E♭
E♭maj9
prophet of doom to wipe ev-'ry smile a-
cradle to tomb isn't that long a
B♭m7
E♭7
A♭
Adim7
To Coda
way;
stay;
Life is a cab-a-
Gm7
C9
Fm7
A♭/B♭
E♭
ret, old chum,
come to the cab-a-ret.

D.S. al Coda
CODA
Gm7
C9
Come taste the
ret, old chum,
Ab
Adim7
only a cab - a -
Gm7
C9
Fm7
ret, old chum, so come to the
Ab/Bb
Eb
Bb9#5
Eb
cab - a - ret.
sfz
8vb

CAN'T HELP LOVIN' DAT MAN

from SHOW BOAT

Lyrics by OSCAR HAMMERSTEIN II
Music by JEROME KERN

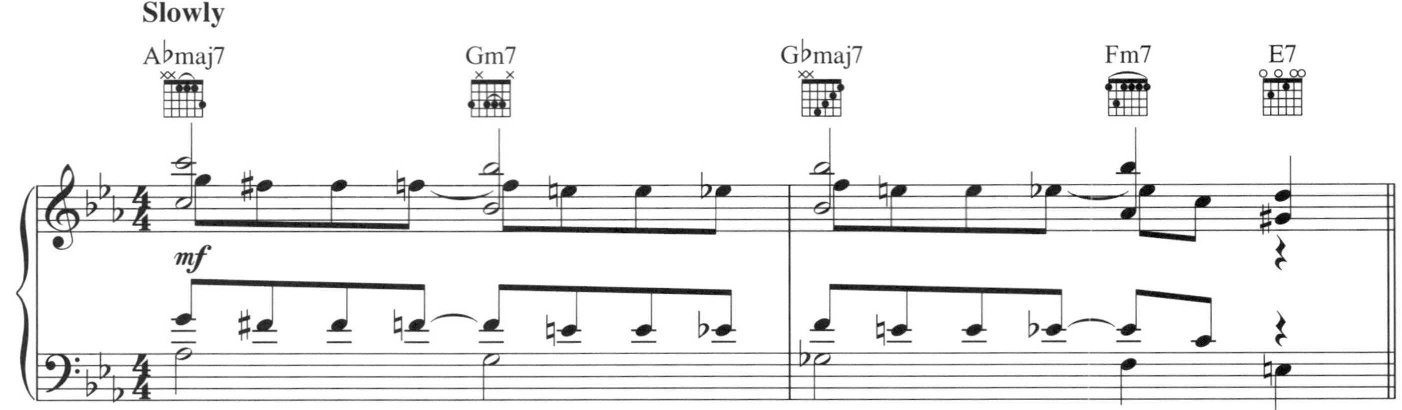

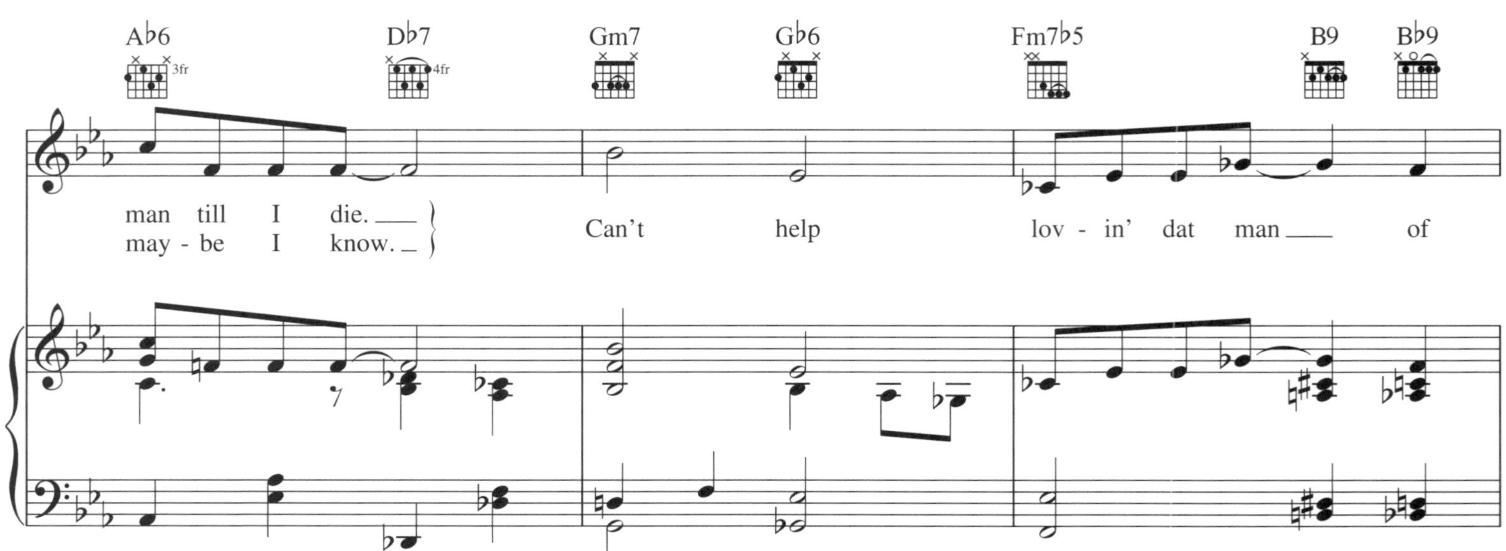

1
2
Eb6
Cm7
Abmaj7
Gm7
Fm7
E7
Eb6
Fm7
mine.
mine.
F#dim7
Eb/G
Ab6
Adim7
When he goes a - way
Eb/Bb
F7/C
Eb/Bb
dat's a rain - y day,
and when he comes
Ebdim7/Bb
Fm7/Bb
Bb7
back dat day is fine,
de sun will shine.

Ebmaj7
Cm7
Fm7
Bb7
He can come home as late as can be,
Ebmaj7
Eb9
Eb7b9
Ab6
Db7
home wid - out him ain't no home to me.
Gm7
Gb6
Fm7b5
B9
Bb9
1
Eb6
Can't help lov - in' dat man of mine.
Gbmaj7
Fm7
E7
2
Eb6
mine.

CIRCLE OF LIFE

Disney Presents THE LION KING: THE BROADWAY MUSICAL

Music by ELTON JOHN
Lyrics by TIM RICE

D
Bm
Em
found. But the sun roll - ing high through the sap - phire sky keeps great and
cresc.
C
A7sus
A7
D
small on the end - less round. It's the cir - cle of life
f
C/D
and it moves us all through de - spair and
G
Asus
hope, through faith and love.

A
D/F♯
B
Till we find our place, on the path un - wind -
Em
Gm6/B♭
D/A
- ing, in the cir - cle,
A
A7
G/D
D
the cir - cle of life.
p
D
Em7/D
A/C♯

D
Bm
Em7
C
Asus
A
D
Em7/D
A/C♯
D
Bm
Em7
cresc.
C
Asus
A7
D
Rafiki & Chorus:
It's the cir - cle of life
f
C/D
and it moves us all
through de - spair and

G
Asus
hope,
through faith and love.
A
F
D7/F♯
D7
Till we find our place on the path un - wind -
ff
Gm
B♭m6/D♭
3fr
F/C
- ing,
in the cir - cle,
Csus
3fr
C7
B♭/F
F
the cir - cle of life.

CLIMB EV'RY MOUNTAIN

from THE SOUND OF MUSIC

Lyrics by OSCAR HAMMERSTEIN II
Music by RICHARD RODGERS

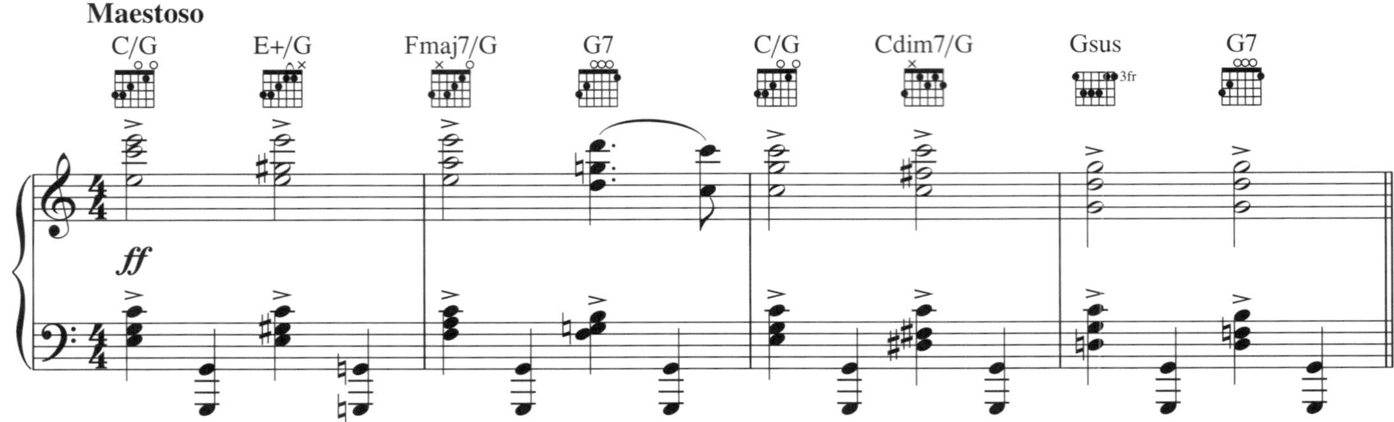

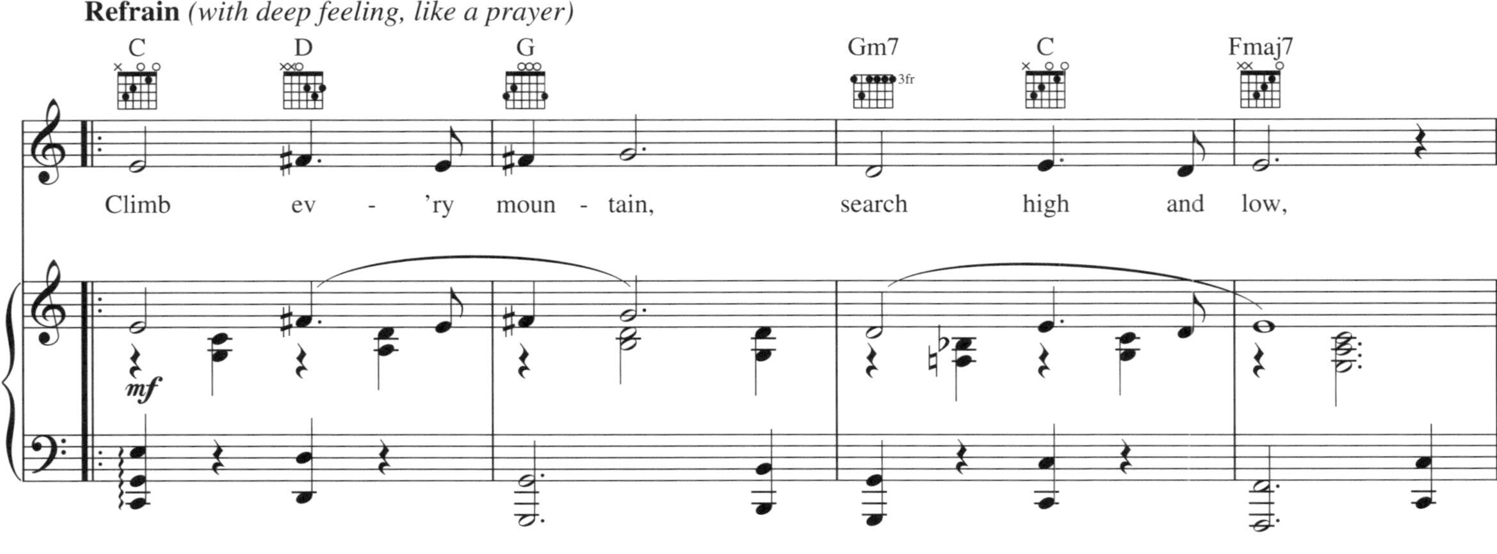

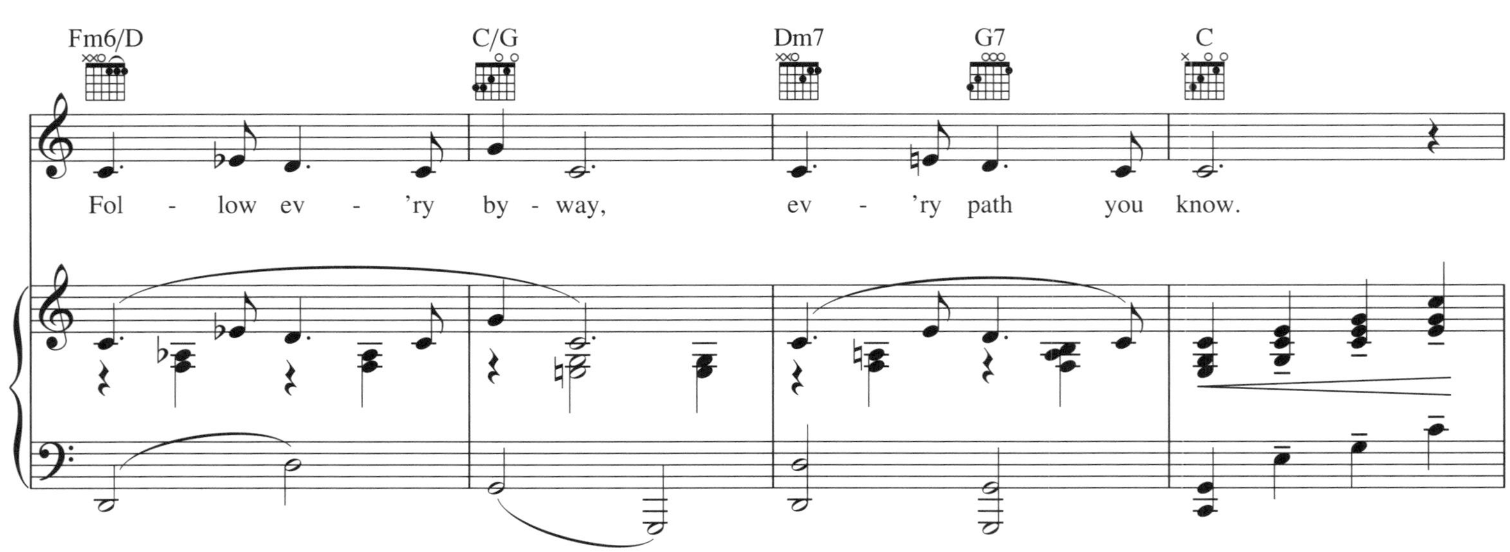

C
D
G
Gm7
3fr
C
Fmaj7
Climb ev - 'ry moun - tain, ford ev - 'ry stream,
più espr.
Fm6/D
C
Dm7
G7
C
C7
Fol - low ev - 'ry rain - bow, till you find your dream! A
mp
F
F/E
Dm
G
C
C/B
dream that will need all the love you can give,
Am7
D7
G
G/F♯
Em
A
Ev - 'ry day of your life for as long as you

Allargando

D D7 G A7 D

live. Climb ev - 'ry moun - tain,

molto cresc. *f* *legato*

Dm7 G Cmaj7 Am Am7/G

ford ev - 'ry stream, Fol - low ev - 'ry

più cresc. e poco a poco allarg.

Dm/F Dm7 C E+ C7♯5 F6 G7

rain - bow till you find your

ff

1 C F G | 2 C Dm7 C

dream! dream!

f *ff marcato*

DANCING QUEEN

from MAMMA MIA!

Words and Music by BENNY ANDERSSON,
BJORN ULVAEUS and STIG ANDERSON

Bm7
E7/B
A
D/A
Watch that scene, diggin' the danc-ing queen.
A
D/A
A
D/A
A
D/A
Fri-day night and the lights are low.
A
F♯m
E
A/E
Look-ing out for a place to go, oh, where they play the right mu-sic.
E
A/E
E
F♯m
E
F♯m
Get-ting in the swing, you come to look for a king.

A
D/A
A
An - y - bod - y could be that guy.
You're a teas - er. You turn 'em on,
Night is young and the mu - sic's
leave 'em burn - ing and then you're
F♯m
E
A/E
E
A/E
E
high.
gone,
With a bit of rock mu - sic,
look - ing out for an - oth - er.
ev - 'ry - thing is fine.
An - y - one will do.
You're in the
F♯m
E
F♯m
Bm7
mood for a dance,
and when you get the chance,
E7
A
you are the danc - ing queen,

D/A
A
D/A
young and sweet, only seventeen.
A
D/A
A
E/G♯
Dancing queen, feel the beat from the tambourine.
F♯m7
A/E
E
C♯7
You can dance. You can jive,
F♯m
B7/D♯
D
having the time of your life. Oh, see that girl.

Bm7
E7/B
A
Watch that scene, digin' the danc - ing queen.
D/A
A
1
D/A
A
D/A
A
D/A
2
D/A
Dig - gin' the
A
D/A
A
Repeat and Fade
danc - ing queen.

DAY BY DAY

from the Musical GODSPELL

Words and Music by
STEPHEN SCHWARTZ

Dm
G
1
Cmaj7
fol - low Thee more near - ly, day by day.
2 Light Rock feeling
Cmaj7
Fmaj7
Gm/F
day by day.
Day by day,
Fmaj7
Gm7/F
B♭maj7
Am7
day by day,
oh, dear Lord, three
Gmaj7
2nd time, play these 4 measures 4 times
Em
things I pray:
to see Thee more

A
Em
A
clear - ly,
love Thee more
dear - ly,
Dm
G
1
Cmaj7
fol - low Thee more
near - ly,
day by day.
2
Cmaj7
Fmaj7
day by day.
Cmaj7
Fmaj7
Amaj7
Day by day,
by
day by day
by
day.

DO I LOVE YOU BECAUSE YOU'RE BEAUTIFUL?

from CINDERELLA

Lyrics by OSCAR HAMMERSTEIN II
Music by RICHARD RODGERS

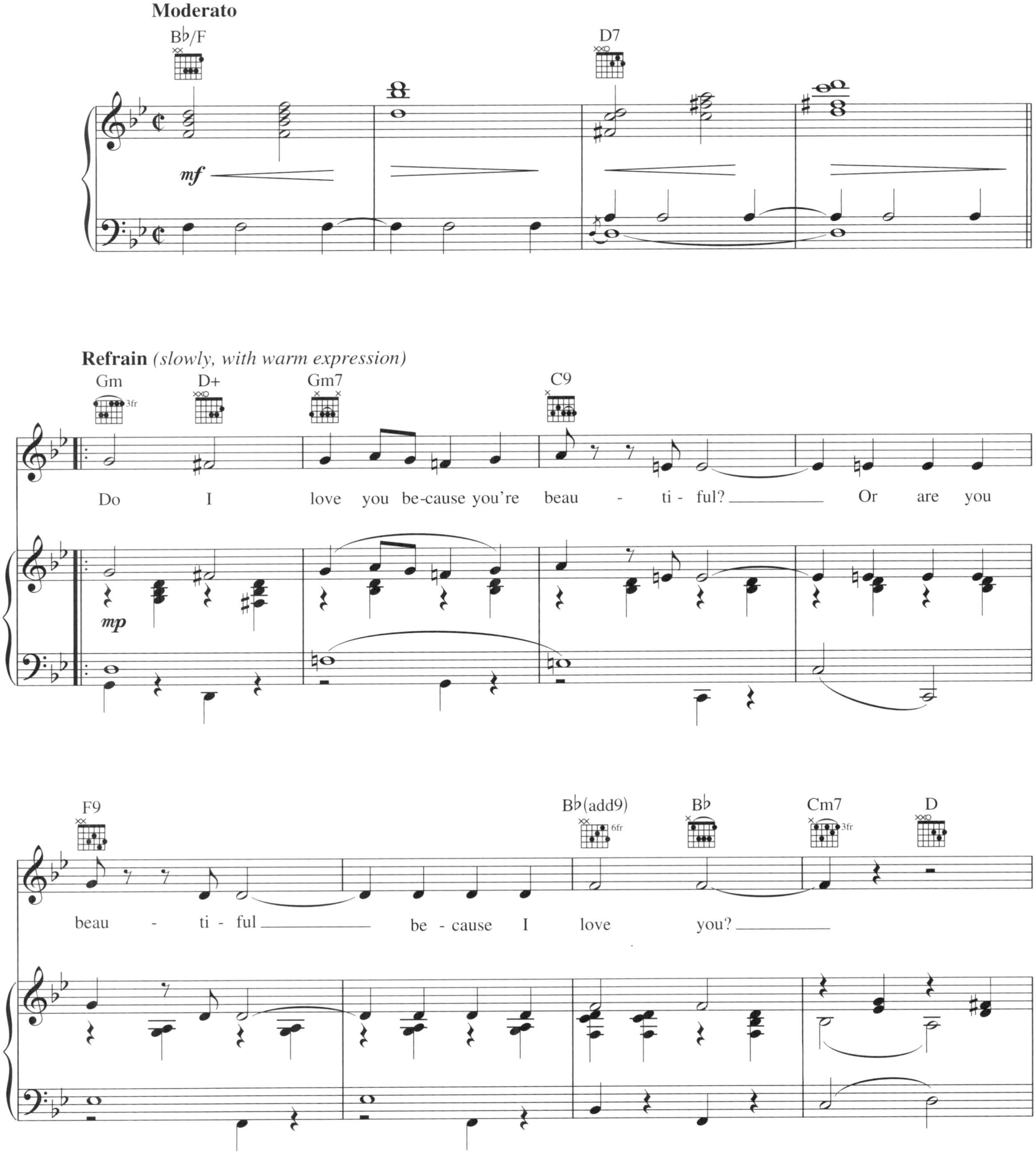

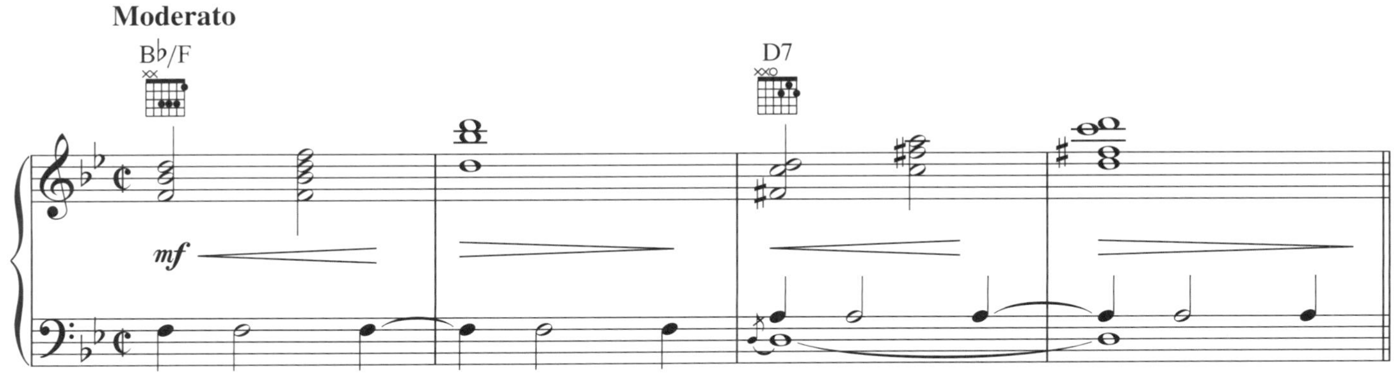

Moderato
B♭/F
D7
mf
Refrain (slowly, with warm expression)
Gm
D+
Gm7
C9
Do I love you be-cause you're beau - ti - ful? Or are you
mp
F9
B♭(add9)
B♭
Cm7
D
beau - ti - ful be - cause I love you?

Gm
D+
Gm7
C9
3fr
Am I making believe I see in you
A girl too
mp
F9
Fm7/B♭
love - ly to be real - ly true?
B♭7
E♭
E♭dim7
3fr
Do I want you be - cause you're
mf espr.
B♭
B♭(add9)
B♭
Gm7
6fr
won - der - ful? Or are you won - der - ful

C9
F9
F7
D7sus
D7
be - cause I want you?
Gm
D+/F♯
Gm7/F
C9
3fr
Are you the sweet in - ven - tion of a lov - er's dream,
mf più espr.
C7
B♭
D+
E♭
F7
3fr
Or are you real - ly as beau - ti - ful as you
f molto espr. e poco rit.
1
2
B♭
D7♯5
B♭
seem?
seem?
a tempo

DON'T CRY FOR ME ARGENTINA

from EVITA

Words by TIM RICE
Music by ANDREW LLOYD WEBBER

D♭
EVA:
It won't be eas - y, you'll think it strange when I
G♭/D♭
mf
try to ex - plain how I feel, that I still need your love af - ter
A♭7/D♭
4fr
3
all that I've done.
D♭
You won't be - lieve me.
B♭m/D♭
All you will see is a girl you once knew, al - though she's dressed up to the
E♭
3fr
E♭/D♭
3

A♭/C
E♭
A♭
nines, at six - es and sev - ens with you.
poco rall.
D♭
G♭/D♭
I had to let it hap - pen, I had to change, could - n't spend all my life down at
p a tempo
A♭7/D♭
D♭
heel, look - ing out of the win - dow, stay - ing out of the sun. So I chose
B♭m/D♭
E♭
E♭/D♭
free - dom, run - ning a - round try - ing ev - 'ry - thing new, but noth - ing im - pressed me at all,

A♭/C
E♭
A♭
3fr
3fr
4fr
I never ex-pec-ted it to.
D♭
B♭m/D♭
D♭
Don't cry for me Ar-gen-ti-na, the truth is I nev-er
p
A♭
B♭m
4fr
left you. All through my wild days, my mad ex-is-tence, I kept my
D♭maj7
G♭maj7
G♭6
G♭
prom-ise, don't keep your dis-tance.

D♭
G♭/D♭
And as for for - tune and as for fame, I
A♭7/D♭
4fr
nev - er in - vit - ed them in, though it seemed to the world _ they were
D♭
B♭m/D♭
all I de - sired. They are il - lu - sions, they're
E♭
3fr
E♭/D♭
not the so - lu - tions they prom - ised to be, the an - swer was here all the

A♭/C
E♭
A♭
3fr
4fr
time, I love you and hope you love me.
rall.
N.C.
CHOIR:
G♭maj7
D♭
Don't cry for me Ar - gen - ti - na. Mm
colla voce
p
E♭m7
D♭
A♭
B♭m
6fr
Ebmaj7
D♭maj7
G♭
D♭
EVA:
Don't cry for me Ar - gen -

ti - na, the truth is I nev - er left you. All through my
A♭7
B♭m
D♭maj7
wild days, my mad ex - is - tence, I kept my prom - ise, don't keep your
G♭maj7
dis - tance. Have I said too much, there's noth - ing more I can think of to
rall.
colla voce
Fm7
G♭maj7
say to you. But all you have to do is
with pedal

D♭
look at me to know that ev - 'ry word is true.
ff
D♭6
D♭
A♭
4fr
B♭m
D♭maj7
G♭maj7
G♭6
G♭maj7
D♭
poco rit.
p

DON'T CRY OUT LOUD
(We Don't Cry Out Loud)
from THE BOY FROM OZ

Words and Music by PETER ALLEN
and CAROLE BAYER SAGER

Cm7
F11
B♭
F/A
3 fr
danced with - out a net up on the wire. I
noth - ing more than saw - dust and some glit - ter. But
Gm
Dm
know a - lot a - bout her 'cause you see,
ba - by can't be bro - ken 'cause you see, she
Gm
C7
F7sus
F7
ba - by is an aw - ful lot like me.
had the fin - est teach - er, that was me. I taught her:
B♭
F/A
Gm
Cm
E♭+/B
Don't cry out loud, just keep it in - side learn how to

Cm/B♭
F11
F
B♭
F/A
Gm
3fr
hide your feel-ings. Fly high and proud and if you should
Cm
3fr
E♭+/B
1
Cm/B♭
F11
Gmaj7
fall re-mem-ber you al-most had it all.
Cm7
3fr
Dm7
Cm7/E♭
F11
2
Cm7/B♭
F11
al - most had it all
Gm
3fr
F♯7sus

B
F♯/A♯
G♯m
4 fr
C♯m
4 fr
E+/B♯
Don't cry out loud, just keep it in - side, learn how to
Fly high and proud, and if you should fall re-mem-ber you

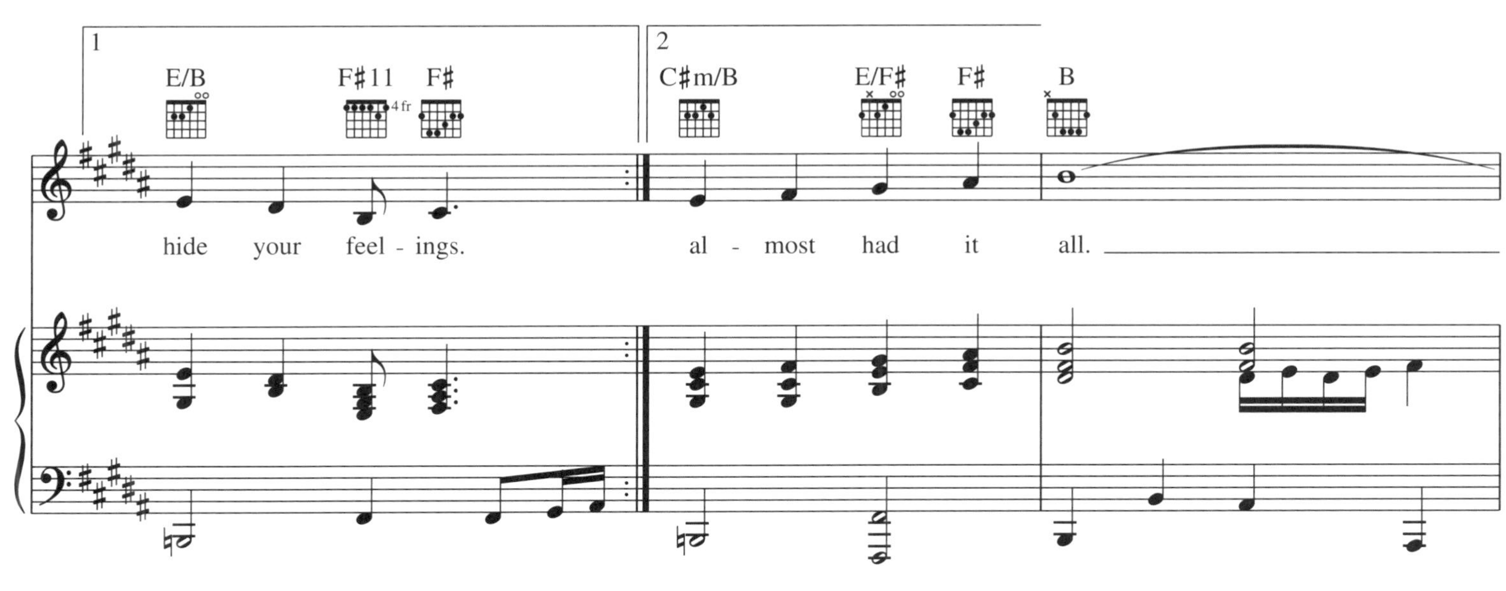
1
2
E/B
F♯11
4 fr
F♯
C♯m/B
E/F♯
F♯
B
hide your feel - ings.
al - most had it all.

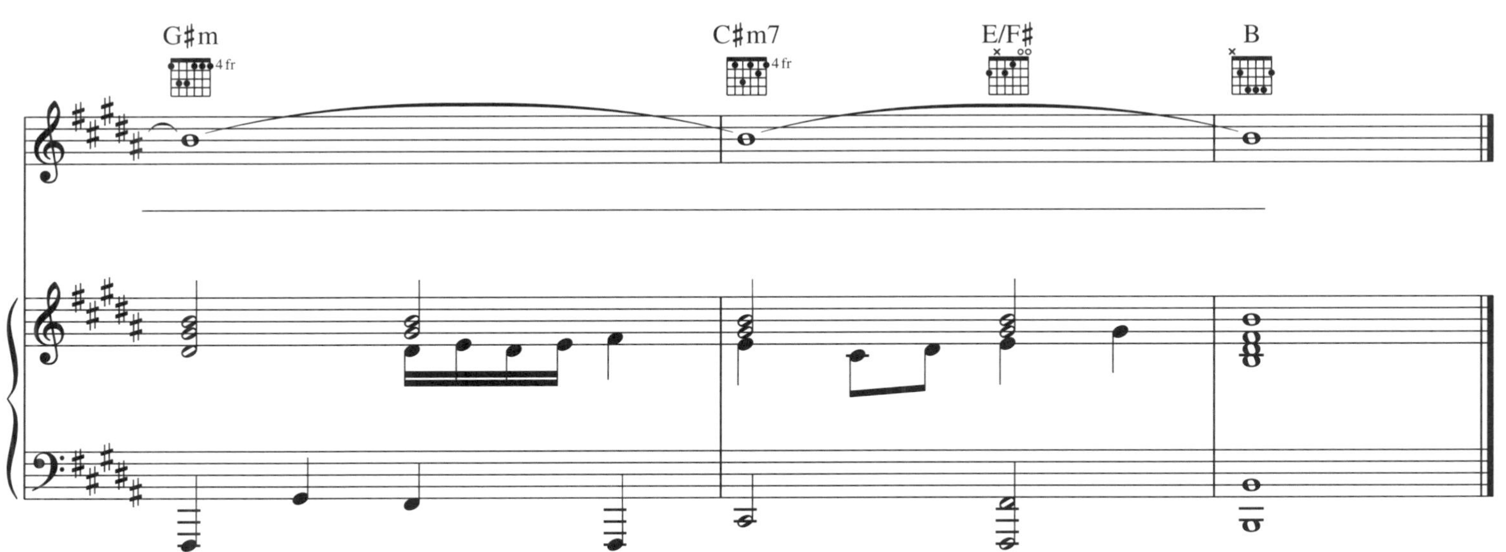
G♯m
4 fr
C♯m7
4 fr
E/F♯
B

EDELWEISS

from THE SOUND OF MUSIC

Lyrics by OSCAR HAMMERSTEIN II
Music by RICHARD RODGERS

B♭
F7/A
B♭/D
E♭/G
Small and white,
Clean and bright,
B♭/F
F7
B♭
You look hap - py to meet me.
F7/A
F7
B♭
Blos - som of snow, may you bloom and grow,
mp
E♭
C/E
F
F7
Bloom and grow for - ev - er.

B♭
Fm6/A♭
E♭/G
E♭m/G♭
E - del - weiss,
E - del - weiss,
B♭/F
F7
B♭
Bless my home - land for - ev - er.
ev - er.
Optional final ending
Gm7
ev - er.
Cm7
E♭/F
F9
rall.

FOLLOW YOUR HEART

from URINETOWN

Music and Lyrics by MARK HOLLMANN
Book and Lyrics by GREG KOTIS

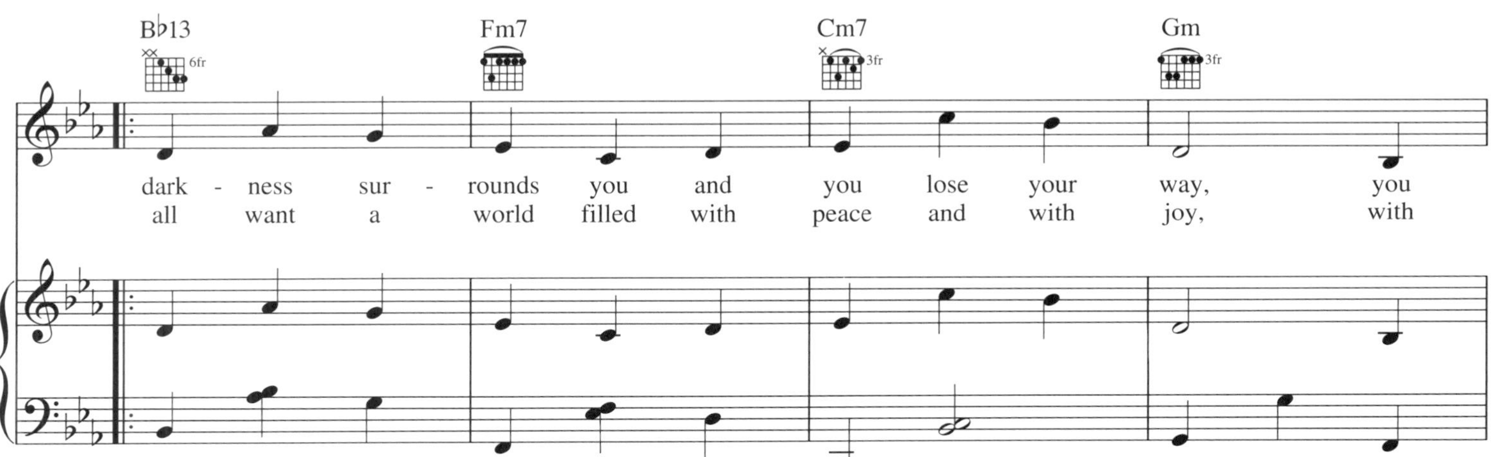

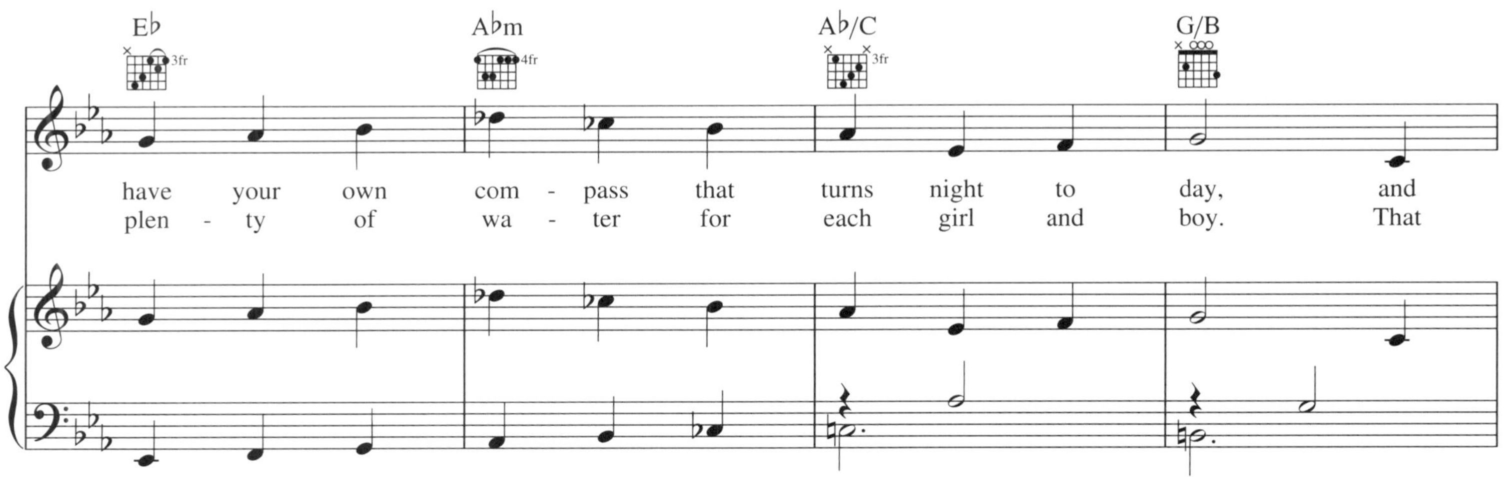

B♭7
Fm7
Cm
Gm
it's e - ven with you be - fore you de - part. Be
bright, shin - ing world is just wait - ing to start. No
E♭
A♭m
1
Cm7
A♭(add2)
still, hear it beat - ing, it's lead - ing you: fol - low your
mean - ness or sor - row, just
E♭
N.C.
heart.
B♭7
rit.

2
A♭/C
Gm/B♭
A♭maj7
We clean - ness to - mor - row, if on - ly you
A♭m6
E♭
N.C.
fol - low your heart.
rit.
B♭7
Fm7/B♭
Gm/B♭
HOPE: Fol - low,
HOPE with BOBBY: Love is
mf

Fm7/B♭
Gm/B♭
Fm7/A♭
Gm/B♭
in - to the o - pen air, far from
kind and con - sid - er - ate, love is
B♭7sus
E♭(add2)/B♭
6fr
Fm7/B♭
E♭maj7/B♭
3fr
squa - lor and noise. Fol - low,
peace - ful and fair. Love can
mp
Fm7/B♭
E♭maj7/B♭
3fr
N.C.
some - one is wait - ing there, some - one who shares all your
creep up so sud - den - ly: when you least think of it,
poco rit.
colla voce
To Coda
B♭7
hopes and your joys.
your love is
a tempo

BOBBY:
Fm7
Cm7
Some - day I'll meet some - one whose heart joins with
Gm
E♭
A♭m
A♭/C
mine, a - or - tas and ar - ter - ies all in - ter -
G/B
B♭7
Fm7
Cm7
twined. They'll beat so much strong - er than they could a -
Gm
E♭
A♭m
A♭/C
part, eight cham - bers of mus - cle to hus - tle the

A♭/B♭
E♭
D.S. al Coda
CODA
B♭7
love in our heart!
there.
a tempo cresc.
Gm/B♭
A♭/B♭
We all want a world filled with peace and with
f
Gm/B♭
E♭maj7/B♭
A♭m
Fm7♭5
joy, with plen - ty of jus - tice for each girl and
Gm/B♭
B♭13
A♭/B♭
boy. That bright, shin - ing world is just

B♭7 Gm/B♭ E♭maj7/B♭ A♭m6 N.C.

wait - ing to start. No an - ger or bad - ness, just

Slower

Gm A♭/E♭ Gm/B♭ A♭6 A♭maj7 A♭m6

laugh - ter and glad - ness, if on - ly I fol - low your

mp *colla voce*

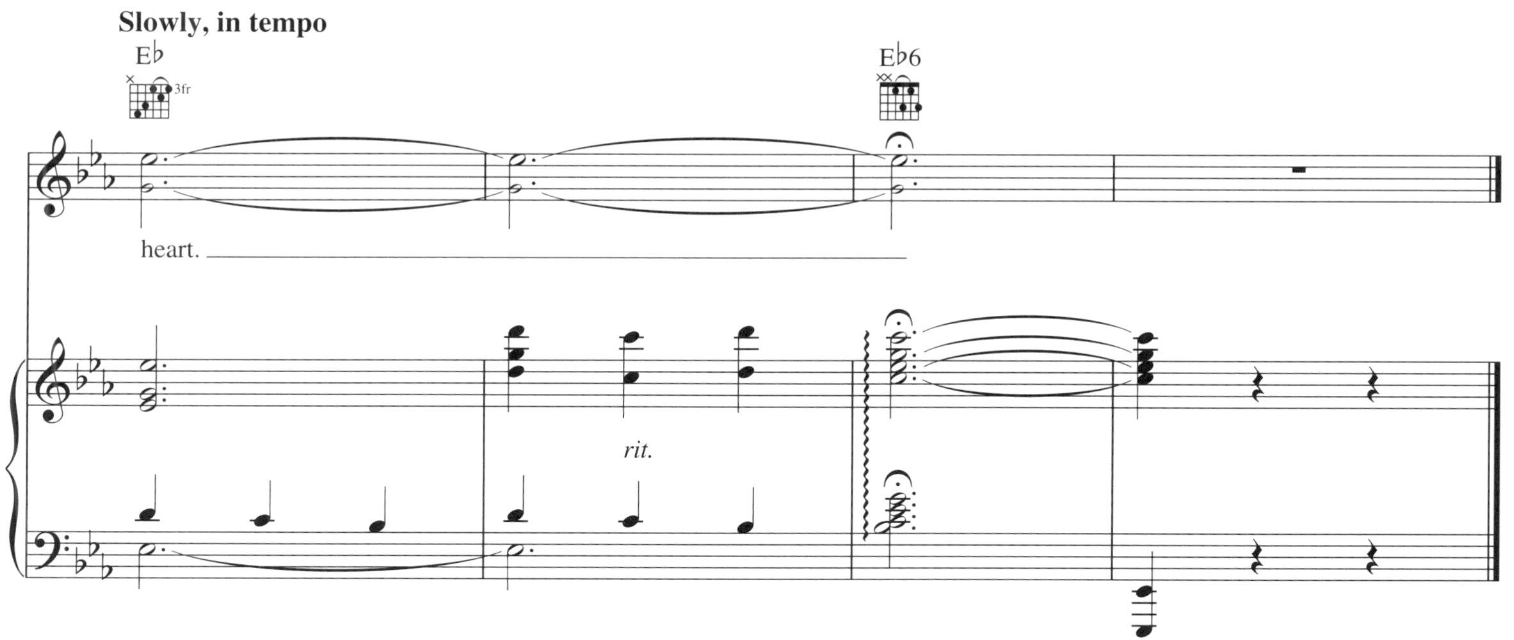

FALLING IN LOVE WITH LOVE

from THE BOYS FROM SYRACUSE

Words by LORENZ HART
Music by RICHARD RODGERS

F7sus
Cm7
3fr
F7
la - dies, let your fin - gers dance,
mf
And
F7sus
Cm7
3fr
F7
keep your hands out of ro - mance.
Love - ly

B♭/D
G7♭9
Cm7
F7
witch - es, let the stitch - es Keep your
Cm7
F7
B♭
fin - gers un - der con - trol. Cut the
Gm
Cm
thread, but leave The
Cm7
F7
B♭
whole heart whole.

F7
Mer - ry maids can sew and sleep,
p
Cm7/F
Fdim7
F7
Wives can on - ly sew and weep!
B♭
B♭maj7
B♭6
B♭
Fall - ing in love with love Is fall - ing for

F7sus
F7
Cm7
3fr
F7
make be - lieve.
F7sus
F7
F7sus
F7
Fall - ing in love with love Is play - ing the
B♭maj7
B♭6
B♭maj7
B♭6
fool;
B♭maj7
B♭6
B♭maj7
B♭6
Car - ing too much is such a ju - ve - nile

Am7
D7
F6/A
D7
fan - cy.
Gdim7
Gm
Cm/G
C7/G
Learn - ing to trust is just For chil - dren in
Cm7/F
Cm7
F7
school.
B♭
B♭maj7
B♭6
B♭
I fell in love with love one night When the

F7sus
F7
Cm7
3fr
F7
moon was full,
F7sus
F7
F7sus
F7
I was un - wise with eyes Un - a - ble to
B♭maj7
B♭6
B♭maj7
B♭6
see.
B♭maj7
B♭6
B♭maj7
B♭6
I fell in love with love, With love ev - er -

Am7
D7
Gmaj7
G7
last - ing,
But
Cm/E♭
3fr
Ddim7
Cm7
3fr
F7
love
fell
out
with
1
B♭
F7
me.
2
B♭
B♭6
me.
Ped.
*

FOR GOOD

from the Broadway Musical WICKED

Music and Lyrics by
STEPHEN SCHWARTZ

Note: When performed as a solo, sing the top melody line throughout.

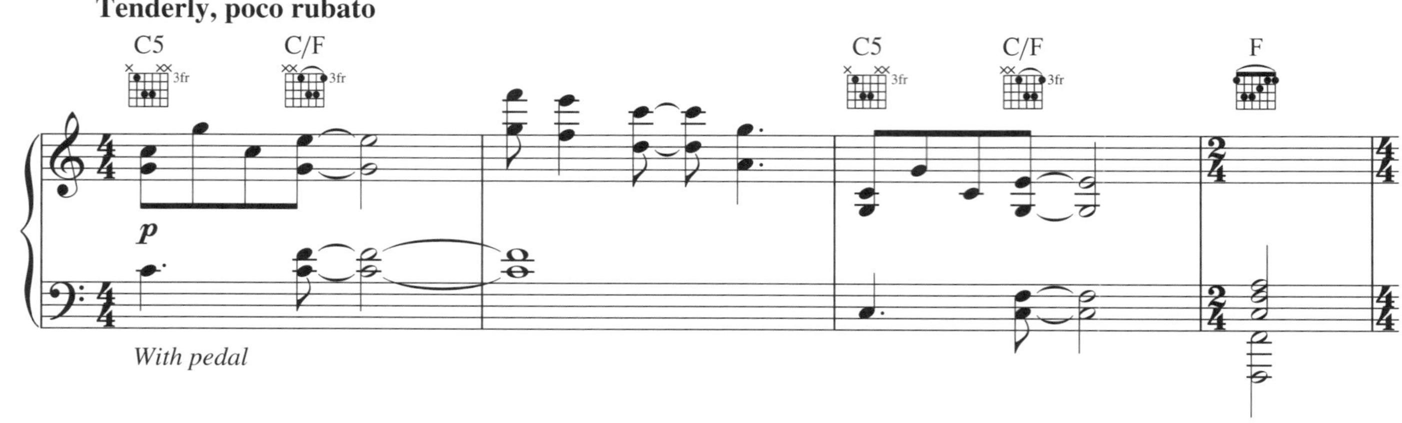

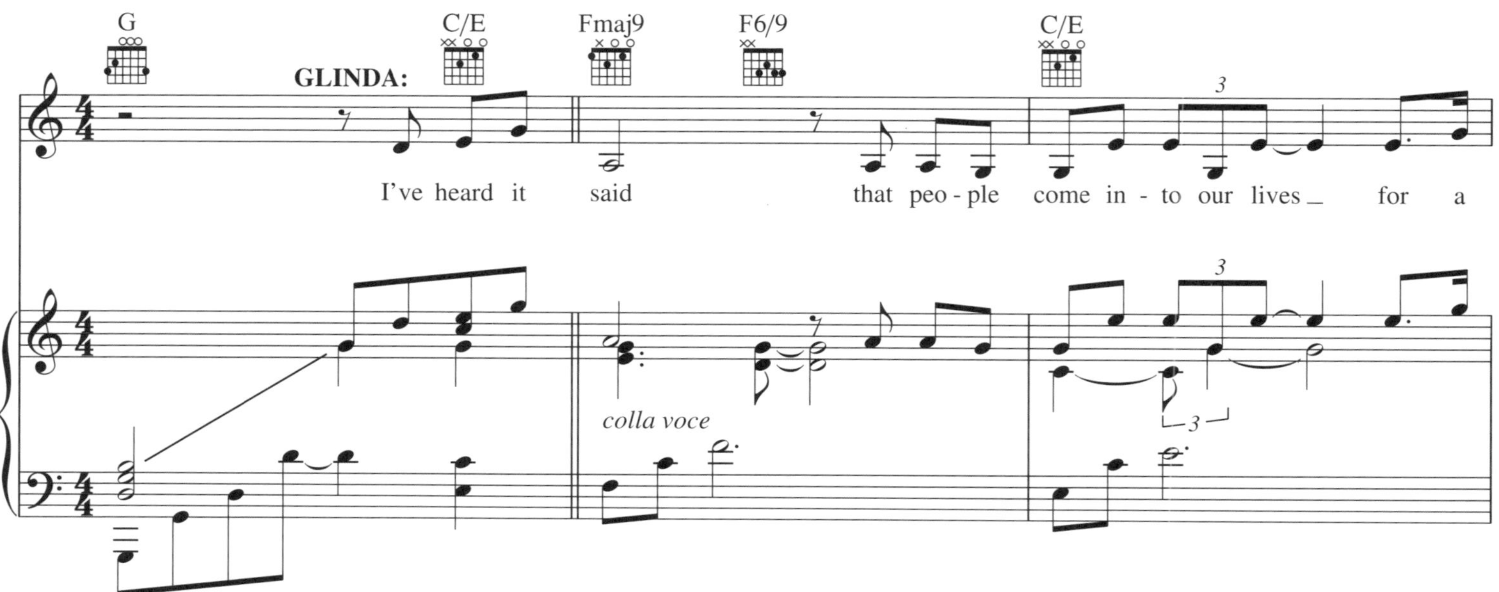

Em7
Am7
D/F♯
Gsus
G
help us most to grow, if we let them, and we help them in re - turn.
C/E
Fsus2
Fm(maj7)
Am/E
Well, I don't know if I be - lieve that's true, But I
A♭
E♭maj7(no3)/A♭
Fm7
E♭/A♭
B♭sus
B♭
know I'm who I am to - day be - cause I knew you... Like a
C/E
Fsus2
Fmaj7(no3)/B♭
C
com - et pulled from or - bit as it pass - es a sun, like a

C/E C/F Bbsus2 Fsus2/A G G/F
stream that meets a boul - der half - way through the wood,
C/E Dm7 Em7 Am(add2)
who can say if I've been changed for the bet - ter? But
Fsus2 C/E F5 C/E Dm7 C/F G5
be-cause I knew you, I have been changed for
rit.
A tempo, warmly
C C/F G C/E
ELPHABA:
good. It well may
mf

Fmaj9
Dm7/F
C
Em
be that we will nev - er meet a - gain in this
Fmaj9
F6/9
C/E
Fsus2
G
C/E
life - time, so let me say be - fore we part: So much of
Fmaj9
F6/9
Em7
me is made of what I learned from you, you'll
Am7
D/F♯
Gsus
3fr
G
be with me like a hand - print on my heart.

C/E
Fsus2
Fm(maj7)
Am
And now what-ev-er way our stor-ies end, I
Ab
Ebmaj7(no3)/Ab
Ab
Fm7
Eb/Ab
4fr
6fr
know you have re-writ-ten mine by be-ing my friend...
Bbsus
Bb
C/E
Fsus2
Like a ship blown from its moor-ing by a
Fmaj7(no3)/Bb
C
C/E
C/F
3fr
wind off the sea, like a seed dropped by a sky-bird

B♭(add9)
F6/A
G
G/F
C/E
Dm7
in a dis - tant wood,
who can say if I've been
Em7
Am7
Fsus2
C/E
changed for the bet-ter? But
be - cause I knew you...
F5
C/E
Dm7(add4)
C/F
G
Più mosso
Fm7
Fm9
GLINDA:
BOTH:
ELPHABA:
Be-cause I knew you...
I have been changed for
good...
And just to
cresc.
B♭
E♭maj7/G
Fm7
Fm9
clear the air,
I ask for - give - ness
for the things I've done you

B♭ B♭/A♭ E♭maj7/G
Gm7 B♭6
GLINDA:
blame me for.
But then, I guess we know there's
Csus C/B♭ F/A
3fr
E♭maj7(no3)/A♭ Fm7(add4)
blame to share,
and none of it seems to mat - ter an - y -
ELPHABA:
and none of it seems to mat - ter an - y -
Fm7/B♭ B♭ B♭/A♭
C/E Fsus2
more.
Like a com - et pulled from or - bit as it
more...
Like a ship blown from its
rit.
a tempo

Csus/B♭ C C/E Fsus2
pass - es a sun like a stream that meets a boul - der
moor - ing by a wind off the sea, like a seed dropped by a
Fsus2/B♭ Fsus2/A G G/F C/E Dm7
half - way through the wood, Who can say if I've been
bird in the wood, Who can say if I've been
senza rit.
dim.
Em7 Am7 Fsus2 C/E G/D
changed for the bet - ter? I do be - lieve I have been changed for the
changed for the bet - ter? I do be - lieve I have been changed for the
mp

Am
Am(add2)
Fsus2
C/E
Fsus2
C/E
bet - ter...
And
be-cause I knew you...
bet - ter...
Be-cause I knew you...
rit. poco a poco
Fsus2
C/E
Dm7(no5)
C/F
Gsus
Be-cause I knew you..
I have been
changed
Be-cause I knew you...
I have been
changed
rit.
Tempo I
C5
C/F
C5
C/F
F(add2)
G
C(add2)
for
good.
for
good.
rit.

I BELIEVE IN YOU

from HOW TO SUCCEED IN BUSINESS WITHOUT REALLY TRYING

By FRANK LOESSER

G
D
G
Cmaj7
Db7
D7
G
You, I Be - lieve In You.
R.H.
G#dim
G
Eb7
Ab
Bbm7
Eb7-5
Ab
I hear the
And when my faith in my fel - low man
Bbm7
Db9
Cm7
F7
Bb
Cm7
F7
all but falls a - part,
I've but to feel your hand
Bb
Gm7
C7
D7sus
D7
G#dim
grasp - ing mine and I take heart,
I take heart.
To see the
rit.

Am7 D9 C C#m7 F#7 Bm C
cool clear eyes of a seek-er of wis-dom and truth,
Bm G#dim Am7 D9 C C#m7 F#7
Yet there's that slam bang tang rem - i - nis - cent of gin and ver -
B C B Cmaj7 Db7 D7 G
mouth. Oh I Be - lieve In You,
Cmaj7 Db7 D7 Cmaj7 D11 Gmaj7
I Be - lieve In You.
R.H.

GETTING TO KNOW YOU

from THE KING AND I

Lyrics by OSCAR HAMMERSTEIN II
Music by RICHARD RODGERS

F♯dim7
C/G
A7
Am7
learn - ing (You'll for - give me if I boast.) And I've now be - come an
D7
Dm7/G
G7
(Spoken)
ex - pert On the sub - ject I like most, Get - ting to know you.
Refrain (gracefully and not fast)
C
Dm7
G7
Get - ting to know you, get - ting to know all a - bout you
mp
tranquillo
Dm7
G7
Dm7
G7
Dm7
G7
C
Get - ting to like you, get - ting to hope you like me

Fmaj7
F6
Getting to know you, Putting it my way, but nicely
F+
F
Am7
D7
Dm7/G
You are precisely My cup of tea!
cresc.
mf
G7
C
Dm7
G7
Getting to know you, getting to feel free and easy
f
p
Dm7
G7
Dm7
G7
Dm7
G7
C7
When I am with you, getting to know what to say.

Fmaj7
F6
Dm7
G7
Have-n't you no - ticed? Sud-den-ly I'm bright and
Cmaj7
C7
F
C
Dm7
G7
breez - y Be-cause of all the beau-ti-ful and new
poco a poco cresc.
C (add9)
Am7
D7
Am7
D7
Dm7
G7
things I'm learn-ing a-bout you day by
C
G7
C
F
C
day. Get-ting to day.
f
p
mf

GLAD TO BE UNHAPPY

from ON YOUR TOES

Words by LORENZ HART
Music by RICHARD RODGERS

F
B♭
F
bad.
But for some-one you a - dore,
mf
Gm7
C7
F
Gm7
E♭
3fr
It's a pleas-ure to be sad.
Like a stray - ing ba - by lamb,
p
C7
Gm7
C7
F/A
Dm7
Gm7
C13
2fr
With no mam-my and no pap - py, I'm so un - hap - py, But oh, so
1
2
F
F
glad!
glad!
mf
mp

HARD CANDY CHRISTMAS

from THE BEST LITTLE WHOREHOUSE IN TEXAS

Words and Music by
CAROL HALL

Fm9
B♭7
C7
get a car, may - be I'll drive so far they'll all lose track.
hit the bars, may - be I'll count the stars un - til the dawn.
Fm9
B♭7
E♭maj9
A♭maj7
Me, I'll bounce right back. May - be I'll sleep real late,
Me, I will go on. May - be I'll set - tle down,
E♭maj9
A♭maj7
Fm9
may - be I'll lose some weight. May - be I'll clear the junk, may - be I'll
may - be I'll just leave town. May - be I'll have some fun, may - be I'll
B♭7
C7sus
C7
Fm9
B♭7
just get drunk on ap - ple wine. Me, I'll be just
meet some - one and make 'em mine. Me, I'll be just

E♭
E♭maj7
A♭/E♭
B♭7/E♭
fine and dan - dy. Lord, it's like a hard can - dy
E♭
Gm
Gm7
A♭
Christ-mas. I'm bare-ly get-ting through to-mor - row, still I won't let
B♭9
B♭7sus
To Coda
1
E♭
B♭
2
E♭maj9
sor-row bring me way down. I'll be
A♭maj7
D.S. al Coda
CODA
E♭
C
F
Fmaj7
I'll be fine and dan -

B♭/F
C7/F
F
-dy. Lord, it's like a hard can - dy Christ - mas. I'm bare - ly get - ting
Am
Am7
B♭
C9
C7sus
through to - mor - row, still I won't let sor - row bring me way down.
Fmaj9
B♭maj7
Fmaj9
I'll be fine.
B♭maj7
Fmaj9
B♭maj7
Fmaj7
I'll be fine.
rit.

HELLO, YOUNG LOVERS

from THE KING AND I

Lyrics by OSCAR HAMMERSTEIN II
Music by RICHARD RODGERS

A
D/F♯
Fdim7
will.
There are new lov - ers now on the
mf
mp
A7/E
E♭7♭5
D
Dm6
same si - lent hill, look - ing on the same blue sea. And I
A
Dm
know Tom and I are a part of them all, and they're all a part of Tom
Gracefully
Fmaj7/G
G7
C
C6
Cmaj7
C6
and me. Hel -
rit.
mf a tempo

C(add9)
C
Cmaj7
C6
lo, young lov - ers, who - ev - er you are, I
p
Cmaj7
C6
G7/B
Fm/C
hope your trou - bles are few.
All my good
G7/B
E♭/B♭
6fr
G7/B
Dm7
Dm7/G
G7
wish - es go with you to - night—
I've been in love like
C
C(add9)
C
Cmaj7
you.
Be brave, young lov - ers, and fol - low your
mf
p

C6
Cmaj7
C6
G7/B
star, be brave and faith - ful and true.
Fm/C
G7/B
E♭/B♭
6fr
G7/B
Dm7
Cling ver - y close to each oth - er to - night—
I've been in
Dm7/G
G7
C
F/A
C7sus/G
3fr
love like you.
I know how it feels to have
mf
mp
F/A
C7sus/G
3fr
F/A
C7sus/G
3fr
C7
F
wings on your heels, and to fly down a street in a trance.

E7
Am
You fly down a street on a chance that you'll meet, and you
Dm7
Dm7/G
G7
meet — not real - ly by chance. Don't
C (add9)
C
Cmaj7
C6
Cmaj7
cry, young lov - ers, what - ev - er you do, don't cry be -
C6
G7/B
Fm/C
G7/B
cause I'm a - lone. All of my mem - 'ries are
p

E♭/B♭
6fr
G7/B
Dm7
G7
hap - py to - night—
I've had a love of my
C7
F/A
Fm/A♭
own,
I've had a love of my
mf
C+/G
C6/G
Dm
E♭/G
3fr
G7
own, like yours,
I've had a love of my
cresc. ed allargando
1
C6
G7
2
C6
own.
Hel -
own.
mf a tempo
p
f

I CAN HEAR THE BELLS

from HAIRSPRAY

Music by MARC SHAIMAN
Lyrics by MARC SHAIMAN and SCOTT WITTMAN

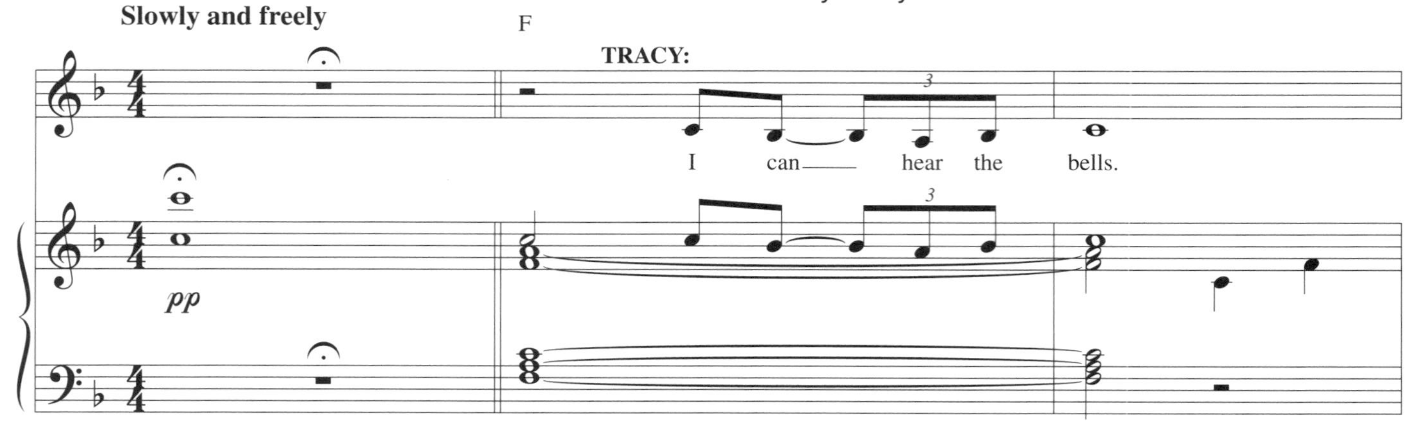

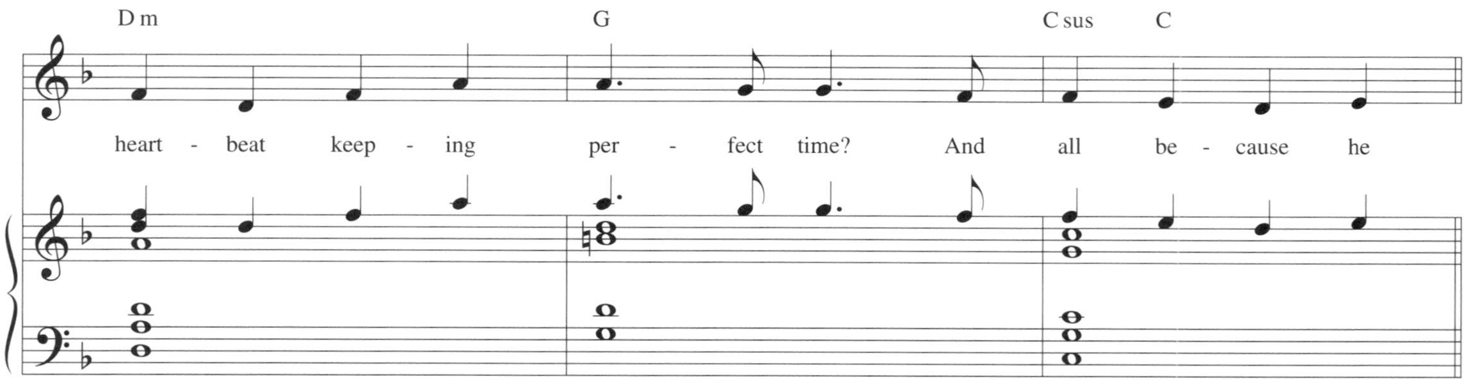

B♭
F/A
heart was un-pre-pared when he tapped me and knocked me off my feet.
G 7sus
G 7
B♭maj9/C
F
One lit-tle touch, now my life's com-plete. 'Cause when he nudged me, love
mp
D m
put me in a fix. Yes, it hit me just like a ton of bricks. Yes, my
B♭
F/A
F/G
G 7
heart burst. Now I know what life's a-bout. One lit-tle touch and love's

F/C C sus C F F/E
knocked me out, and I can hear the bells. My head is spin - ning.
D m D m/C B♭
I can hear the bells. Some - thing's be - gin - ning. Ev - 'ry - bod - y says that a
F/A F/G G 7 D m/C C B♭/C C
girl who looks like me can't win his love. Well, just wait and see, 'cause
F F/E D m
I can hear the bells. Just hear them chim - ing. I can hear the bells. My
mf

D m/C B♭ F/A
tem - p'ra - ture's climb - ing. I can't con - tain my joy 'cause I fin - 'ly found the boy I've been
F/G G7 C7sus F
miss - in'. Lis - ten! I can hear the be - ells.
(ding!)
mp
B♭/C F D♭sus D♭
G♭ G♭/F E♭m
Round one, he'll ask me on a date, and then round two, I'll
f mf

C♭
G♭/B♭
primp, but won't be late be-cause round three's when we kiss in-side his car. Won't
G♭/A♭
A♭7
G♭/D♭
D♭
D♭sus2
D♭
G♭
go all the way, but I'll go pret-ty far. Then round four, he'll
mf
G♭/F
E♭m
ask me for my hand, and then round five, we'll book the wed-ding band, so by
C♭
G♭/B♭
G♭/A♭
A♭7
round six, Am-ber, much to your sur-prise, this heav-y-weight cham-pi-on

E♭m/D♭ D♭ C♭/D♭ D♭
G♭
G♭/F
takes the prize and I can hear the bells. My ears are ring - ing.
E♭m
E♭m/D♭ C♭
I can hear the bells. The brides - maids are sing - ing. Ev - 'ry - bod - y says that a
G♭/B♭
A♭7sus A♭7
E♭m/D♭ D♭ C♭/D♭ D♭
guy who's such a gem won't look my way. Well, the laugh's on them 'cause
G♭
G♭/F E♭m
I can hear the bells. My fa - ther will smile… I can hear the bells. …as he
f
mf

E♭m/D♭
C♭
G♭/B♭
walks me down the aisle. My moth-er starts to cry, but I can't see 'cause Link and I are French-
mf
G♭/A♭
A♭7
D♭7sus
G♭
kiss - in'. Lis - ten! I can hear the bells.
(ding!)
mp
C♭/G♭
G♭
D sus
D
G
G/F♯
E m
I can hear the bells. My head is reel - in'. I can hear the bells. I
ff

Em/D C G/B
can't stop the peal - in'. Ev - 'ry - bod - y warns that he won't like what he'll see, but
G/A A7 Em/D D C/D D G
I know that he'll look in - side of me. Yeah, I can hear the bells. To -
G/F♯ Em Em/D
day's just the start 'cause I can hear the bells, and 'til death do us part. And
C G/B Am7
e - ven when we die we'll look down from up a - bove, re - mem - ber - ing the night that we
f
ff
mp

G/B
G7/B
C
two fell in love. We both will share a tear, and he'll
G/B
G/A
A
D7sus
whis - per as we're rem - i - nisc - in'. Lis - ten! I can hear the
colla voce
(ding!)
G
G7/F
Em7
bells. I can hear the bells.
rit.
Cm/E♭
G
I can hear the bells.

IF I WERE A BELL

from GUYS AND DOLLS

By FRANK LOESSER

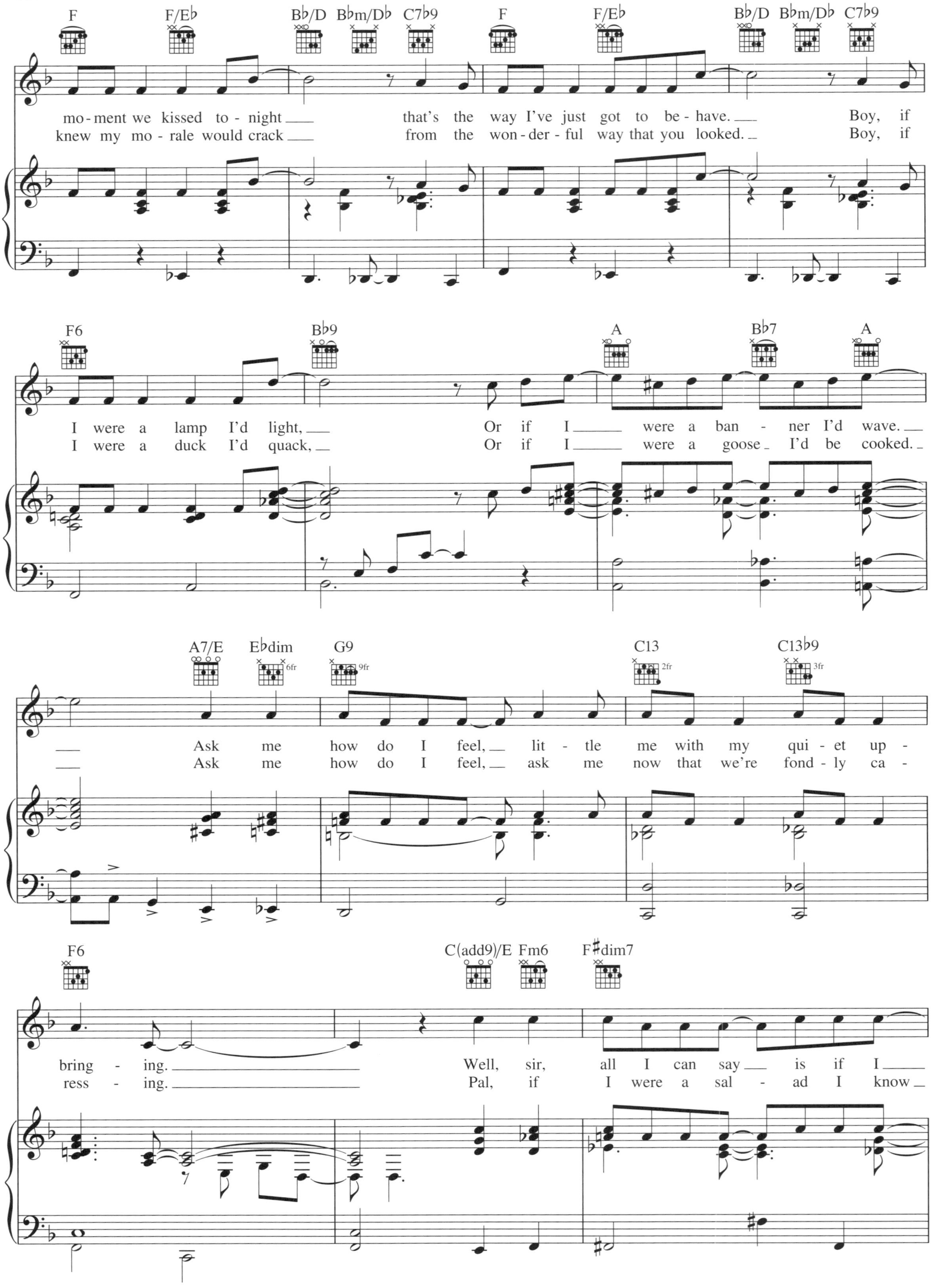
F F/E♭ B♭/D B♭m/D♭ C7♭9 F F/E♭ B♭/D B♭m/D♭ C7♭9
mo-ment we kissed to-night that's the way I've just got to be-have. Boy, if
knew my mo-rale would crack from the won-der-ful way that you looked. Boy, if
F6 B♭9 A B♭7 A
I were a lamp I'd light, Or if I were a ban-ner I'd wave.
I were a duck I'd quack, Or if I were a goose I'd be cooked.
A7/E E♭dim G9 C13 C13♭9
6fr 9fr 2fr 3fr
Ask me how do I feel, lit-tle me with my qui-et up-
Ask me how do I feel, ask me now that we're fond-ly ca-
F6 C(add9)/E Fm6 F♯dim7
bring-ing. Well, sir, all I can say is if I
ress-ing. Pal, if I were a sal-ad I know

E♭7
D7
G9
Gm7♭5/D♭
C7
C7♭9
were a gate I'd be swing - ing.
I'd be splash - ing my dress - ing.
And if
Or if
F
F/E♭
B♭/D
A♭dim7
F/A
E7♯5
I were a watch I'd start pop - ping my spring,
I were a sea - son I'd sure - ly be spring,
E♭7
D9
D7♭9
Dm7/G
G9♭5
Fmaj7
Dm7
B♭maj7
C9
Or if I were a bell I'd go ding dong ding dong
Or if I were a bell I'd go ding dong ding dong
F6/9
A♭dim
Gm9
A7/E
E♭dim
F6/9
E♭6/9
F6/9
ding. Ask me
ding.
ff

I DON'T KNOW HOW TO LOVE HIM

from JESUS CHRIST SUPERSTAR

Words by TIM RICE
Music by ANDREW LLOYD WEBBER

F♯m7
Bm
G
D/F♯
Em
D
Asus(add9)
A
seen my-self I seem like some-one else
D
G
D
G
D
G
G6
G
I don't know how to take this I don't see why he
D/A
A
D/F♯
A
D
A
moves me. He's a man, he's just a man, and I've
F♯m7
Bm
F♯m7
Bm
G
D/F♯
Em
D
had so man-y men be-fore in ver-y man-y

Asus(add9)
A
G
D/F♯
Em7
D
G
ways. He's just one more.
Should I bring him down
Instrumental
p
mp
cresc. poco a poco
F♯7
Bm
Bm/A
G
should I scream and shout? Should I speak of love, let my feel-ings out?
Instrumental ends
D/A
C
G
D
G
D/F♯
I nev-er thought I'd come to this. What's it all a-
ff
f
dim. poco a poco
Em
Asus(add9)
A
D
G
D
bout?
Don't you think it's rath-er
Yet if he said he
mp

G D G G6 G D/A A
fun - ny I should be in this po - si - tion? I'm the
loved me, I'd be lost I'd be fright - ened. I could - n't
D/F♯ A D A F♯m7 Bm
one who's al - ways been So calm and cool
cope, just could - n't cope. I'd turn my head,
F♯m7 Bm7 G D/F♯ Em D Asus A G D/F♯ Em7
no lov - er's fool run - ning ev - 'ry show. He scares me
I'd back a - way, I would - n't want to know. He scares me
1 D
so.
2 D G D/F♯ Em7 D G D/F♯ Em7 D
so. I want him so. I love him so.
mf

I DREAMED A DREAM

from LES MISÉRABLES

Music by CLAUDE-MICHEL SCHÖNBERG
Lyrics by ALAIN BOUBLIL,
JEAN-MARC NATEL and HERBERT KRETZMER

Cm7
E♭/B♭
A♭
A♭/G
die.
I dreamed that God would be for -
Fm7
B♭
E♭
E♭/D
giv - ing.
Then I was young and un - a -
Cm
E♭/B♭
A♭
A♭/G
fraid,
and dreams were made and used and
Fm7
B♭6
E♭
E♭/D
wast - ed.
There was no ran - som to be

Cm7
E♭/B♭
A♭
A♭/G
Fm7
B♭
paid, no song un - sung, no wine un - tast - ed.
C
C/E
Fm
C
C7
But the ti - gers come at night with their voic - es soft as
poco più mosso
F
F/A
B♭
B♭/D
E♭m
thun - der, as they tear your hope a - part,
B♭
E♭
Fm/E♭
E♭
A♭/E♭
as they turn your dream to shame.

B♭
E♭
E♭/D
He / She slept a sum - mer by my
rall.
a tempo
Cm
E♭/B♭
A♭
A♭/G
Fm7
B♭6
side.
He / She filled my days with end - less won - der.
E♭
E♭/D
Cm7
E♭/B♭
A♭
B♭6
He / She took my child - hood in his / her stride,
but he / she was gone when au - tumn
E♭
B♭/D
B♭m6/D♭
C
came.
poco accel. e cresc.

F
F/E
Dm7
F/C
And still I dreamed {he'd / she'd} come to me,
mf più mosso
Bb
Bb/A
Gm7
3fr
C
that we would live the years to - geth - er.
But there are dreams that can - not
Dm7
be,
and there are storms we can - not weath - er.
cresc.
I had a dream my life would
f
appassionato

B♭
B♭/A
Gm7
3fr
B♭/C
C
be
so dif - f'rent from this hell I'm
3
F
F/E
Dm7
F/C
liv - ing, so dif-f'rent now from what it seemed.
cresc.
ff
dim.
poco rall.
B♭
C
F
F/E
Now life has killed the dream I dreamed.
mp
p
a tempo
Dm7
F/A
B♭
C9
F
rall.

I ENJOY BEING A GIRL

from FLOWER DRUM SONG

Lyrics by OSCAR HAMMERSTEIN II
Music by RICHARD RODGERS

C7
gait With my hips kind of swiv - el - ly and
Fmaj7
swerv - y. I a - dore be - ing dressed in some - thing
G7/F
fril - ly When my date comes to get me at my place. Out I
B♭m6/F
F
F6
go with my Joe or John or Bill - y, Like a fil - ly who is

Fmaj7 F C7 B♭/D D♯m6 C7/E C7

read - y for the race! When

Refrain *(brightly)*

F6

mf

I have a brand - new hair - do With my

C7

eye - lash - es all in curl, I

F D7 Gm B♭m/D♭

float as the clouds on air do, I en -

F/C
C7
F6
joy be - ing a girl!
F
F6
When men say I'm cute and
C7
fun - ny And my teeth are - n't
teeth but pearl, I

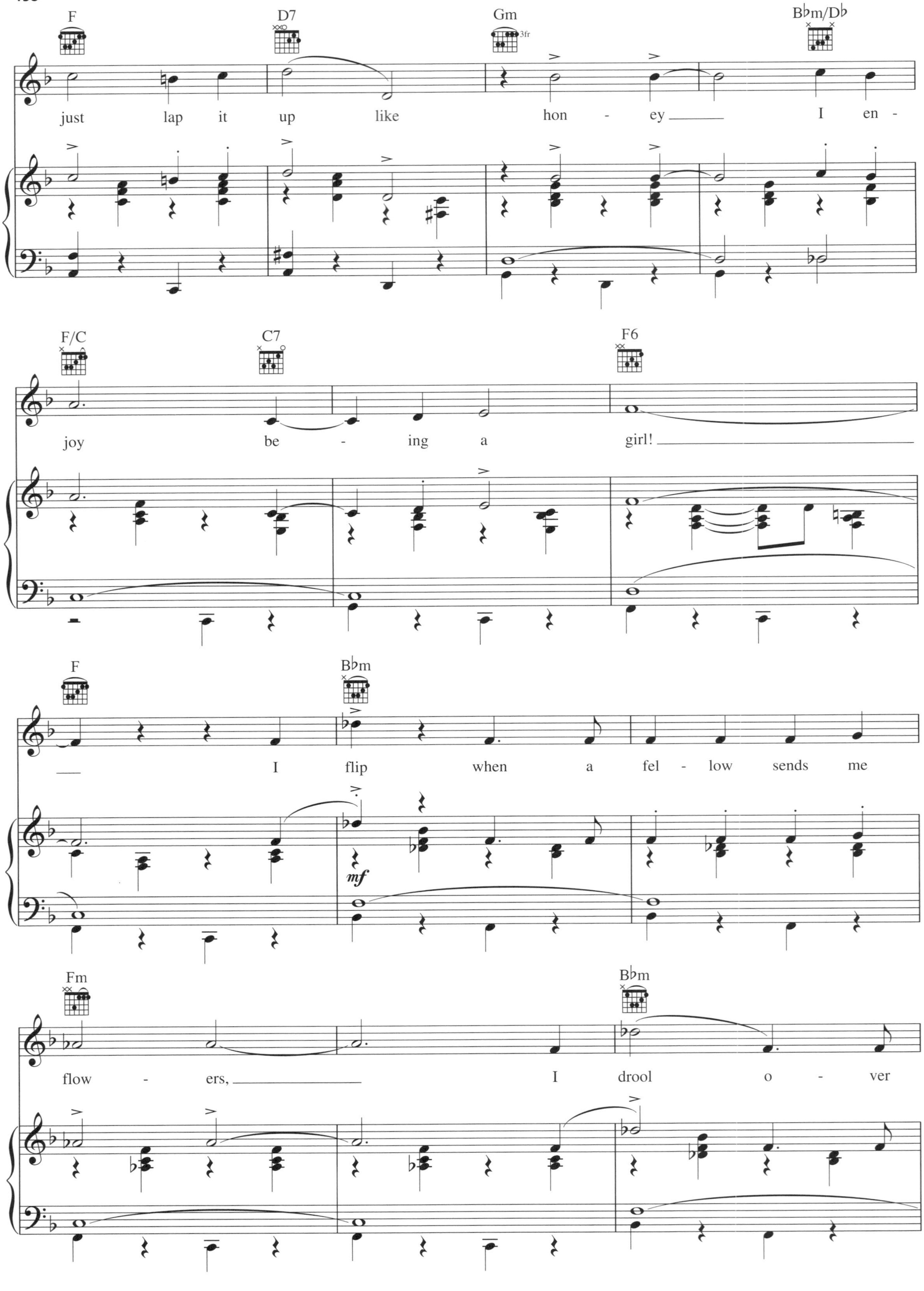
F D7 Gm B♭m/D♭
3fr
just lap it up like hon - ey I en -
F/C C7 F6
joy be - ing a girl!
F B♭m
I flip when a fel - low sends me
mf
Fm B♭m
flow - ers, I drool o - ver

Fm
Fm7
Fm6
Fm
dress - es made of lace,
I
D♭
A♭
A♭maj7
talk on the tel - e - phone for ho - urs
A♭6
A♭
G7
With a pound and a half of cream up - on my
C
B♭
C9
F6
face!
I'm strict - ly a
f
mf

fe - male fe - male And my
C7
fu - ture I hope will be In the
F
D7
Gm
3fr
home of a brave and free male
G9
9fr
F
Dm
Who'll en - joy be - ing a

Gm
3fr
B♭m/D♭
F/C
F7
F6
guy hav - ing a girl
C13
2fr
1
F
like
me.
f
Ped.
A♭7
4fr
C13
2fr
C7
2
F
When
me.
f
Ped.
sf

I'LL BE SEEING YOU

from RIGHT THIS WAY

Lyric by IRVING KAHAL
Music by SAMMY FAIN

B♭/F
F7
B♭
But when the morn-ing chimes ring sweet a-
Slowly
Fm7/B♭
B♭7
E♭
3 fr
G7
Fm
C7
gain: I'll be see-ing you In all the old fa-
p - mf
Fm
C7
Fm
B♭7
mil-iar plac-es That this heart of mine em-brac-es
E♭
3 fr
Cm
3 fr
all day thru: In that small ca-fé, The

Fm7
Fm7/B♭
B♭7
park a - cross the way, the chil - dren's
B♭7♯5
E♭
3 fr
B♭9♯5
ca - rou - sel, The chest - nut trees, the wish - ing well.
rit.
E♭
3 fr
G7
Fm
C7
I'll be see - ing you In ev - 'ry love - ly
a tempo
Fm
C7
Fm
B♭7
sum - mer's day, In ev - 'ry - thing that's light and gay, I'll

Gm7♭5
5 fr
C7
Fm
al - ways think of you that way I'll find you in the
cresc.
G7
Cm
3 fr
F9
morn - ing sun; And when the night is new, I'll be
8va
loco
mf
rit.
p
Fm7
Fm7♭5
1
E♭
3 fr
B♭7
look - ing at the moon But I'll be see - ing you!
3
cresc.
Fm7
B♭7
B♭7♯5
2
E♭sus
E♭
3 fr
Fm7
E♭6
you!
f
8vb

I'M GONNA WASH THAT MAN RIGHT OUTA MY HAIR

from SOUTH PACIFIC

Lyrics by OSCAR HAMMERSTEIN II
Music by RICHARD RODGERS

F
C9
F
Gm7
F/A
C7
send him on his way. I'm gon - na
F
Gm7
F/A
B♭
C7
F
Gm7
wave that man right out - a my arms, I'm gon - na wave that man right
F/A
B♭
C7
F
Gm7
F/A
B♭
out - a my arms, I'm gon - na wave that man right out - a my arms, And
F
C7
F7
send him on his way.

B♭
Don't try to patch it up, Tear it up, tear it up! Wash him out, dry him out,
mf
F
G7
Push him out, fly him out, Can - cel him and let him
C
A♭
4fr
G♭
C
C7
F
Gm7
go! Yea, sis - ter! I'm gon - na wash that man right
mp
F/A
B♭
C7
F
Gm7
F/A
B♭
C7
out - a my hair, I'm gon - na wash that man right out - a my hair, I'm gon - na

To Coda
F
Gm7
F/A
B♭
F
C7
wash that man right out - a my hair, And send him on his
Interlude
F
B♭
Cm7
B♭7
F7
way. If the man don't un - der - stand you If you
B♭
F7
B♭
E♭
E♭/D
fly on sep - 'rate beams, Waste no time,
Cm7
E♭
B♭
B♭maj7/A
Gm
B♭6
Make a change, Ride that man right off your range,

C7
G♭7
F7
Rub him out - a the roll - call And drum him out - a your
dreams. If you laugh at dif - f'rent com - ics If you
B♭
Cm7
B♭7
F7
root for dif - f'rent teams,
B♭
F7
B♭
E♭
E♭maj7
Waste no time,
Cm7
E♭
B♭
B♭maj7
Gm
B♭6
Weep no more,
Show him what the door is for!

C7
Gb7
F7
Rub him out - a the roll - call
And drum him out - a your
mf
G7b5/Db
8fr
dreams.
Oh,
no!
Oh,
C7
D.S. al Coda
no!
I'm gon - na
mp
CODA
F
Ab
4fr
send him
G
Gb7
F
on his way.
f

IF I LOVED YOU

from CAROUSEL

Lyrics by OSCAR HAMMERSTEIN II
Music by RICHARD RODGERS

A
If I loved you!
If I loved you!
Oh,
Oh,
D/F#
C(add9)/G
C/G
G7
some - how I can see just ex - ack - ly how I'd be.
p
rit.
Refrain (with great warmth and slowly)
C
Cdim7
C/E
E+
If I loved you, Time and a - gain I would try to say
mf
Dm/F
D#dim7
C/E
Em
All I'd want you to know.
cross hands

C
Cdim7
C/E
If I loved you,
Words _ would-n't come _ in an
E+
Dm/F
D♯dim7
C/E
eas - y way, 'Round in cir - cles I'd go. ___
cresc.
E+
Am
Dm
C♯7
___ Long - in' to tell you, but a - fraid and
mf espr.
C/G
Dm/F
B♭
D/A
shy, I'd let my gold - en chanc - es pass me

G
G7
C
Cdim7
C/E
by! Soon you'd leave me, off you would go in the
E+
Dm/F
D♯dim7
C/G
Em
mist of day, Nev - er, nev - er to know
C
Em
Dm/F
C/E
Dm7
Dm7/G
G7
How I loved you, If I
mf
molto espr.
f
rit.
1
C
Dm7/G
G7
loved you.
2
C
loved you.
a tempo
L.H.

IF I WERE A RICH MAN

from the Musical FIDDLER ON THE ROOF

Words by SHELDON HARNICK
Music by JERRY BOCK

Cm
D7
G7
To Coda
C
Guitar Tacet
bid - dy, bid - dy rich,
dig - guh, dig - guh, dee - dle dai - dle
man.
I'd
build
a
rall.
Quasi rubato
Fm
Bb7
Ebmaj7
Bbm6
C7
big tall house with rooms by the doz - en,
Right in the mid - dle of the town;
A
Fm
G7
C
C7
fine tin roof with real wood - en floors be - low.
There could be
Fm
Bb7
Ebmaj7
Bbm6
C7
one long stair - case just go - ing up and one e - ven long - er com - ing down;
And

Fm
F♯dim
G7
C7
one more lead - ing no - where just for show. I'd fill my
rall.
F
G7
C
A7
yard with chicks and tur - keys and geese And ducks for the town to see and hear;
Dm7
G7
C
C7
Squawk - ing just as nois - i - ly as they can. And each loud
Fm
B♭7
E♭maj7
B♭m6
C7
quack and cluck and gob - ble and honk Will land like a trum-pet on the ear; As
(imitate sounds)

Fm
F#dim
G7
D.S. al Coda
if to say here lives a wealth - y man.
(Sigh)
rall.
Quasi rubato
CODA
C
Guitar Tacet
Fm
Bb7
man. I see my wife, my Gold - e, look - ing like a rich man's
Ebmaj7
Bbm6
C7
Fm
G7
wife with a prop - er dou - ble chin; Su - per - vis - ing meals to her heart's de -
C
C7
Fm
Bb7
light. I see her put - ting on airs and strut - ting like a pea - cock

Ebmaj7
Bbm6
C7
Fm
F#dim
Oy! What a hap-py mood she's in. Scream-ing at the ser-vants day and
G7
C7
Rubato
night. The most im-por-tant men in town will come to fawn on — me;
Fm
Db
They will ask me to ad-vise them, — Like Sol-o-mon the wise, "If you
Bbm
C7
please, Reb Tev-ye, par-don me, Reb Tev-ye." Pos-ing prob-lems what would cross a rab-bi's eyes.

Freely
Deliberately (in tempo)
Fm7
Bb7
Boi, boi, boi, boi, boi, boi, boi, boi, boi.
And it won't make one bit of dif - f'rence
Ebmaj7
Bbm6
C7
Fm
F#dim
If I an - swer right or wrong?
When you're rich, they think you real - ly
G7
C7
Reflective
F
G7
know.
If I were rich, I'd have the time that I lack, To
rall.
p
C
A7
Dm7
G7
sit in the syn - a - gogue and pray;
And may - be have a seat by the east - ern

C
C7
Fm
Bb7
wall.
And I'd dis - cuss the ho - ly books with the learn - ed
Ebmaj7
C7
Fm
F#dim
G7
men sev - en ho - urs ev' - ry day;
This would be the sweet - est thing of all.
Tempo I
C
(Sigh)
If I were a rich man,
Dai - dle, dee - dle, dai - dle,
dig - guh, dig - guh, dee - dle, dai - dle,
G7
Cm
D7
dum.
All day long I'd bid - dy, bid - dy bum,
If I were a wealth - y

G7
C
man.
Would-n't have to work hard,
Dai-dle, dee-dle, dai-dle
dig-guh, dig-guh, dee-dle, dai-dle,
8va
Rubato
G7
Cm
G7
dum.
Lord, who made the
li-on and the lamb,
You de - creed I
8va
Cm
G7
Cm
A7-5
D7-5
G7
should be what I am;
Would it spoil some
vast e-ter-nal plan,
If I were a wealth - y
15ma
8va
C
G7
C
man?
8va
a tempo
8va

THE IMPOSSIBLE DREAM
(The Quest)
from MAN OF LA MANCHA

Lyric by JOE DARION
Music by MITCH LEIGH

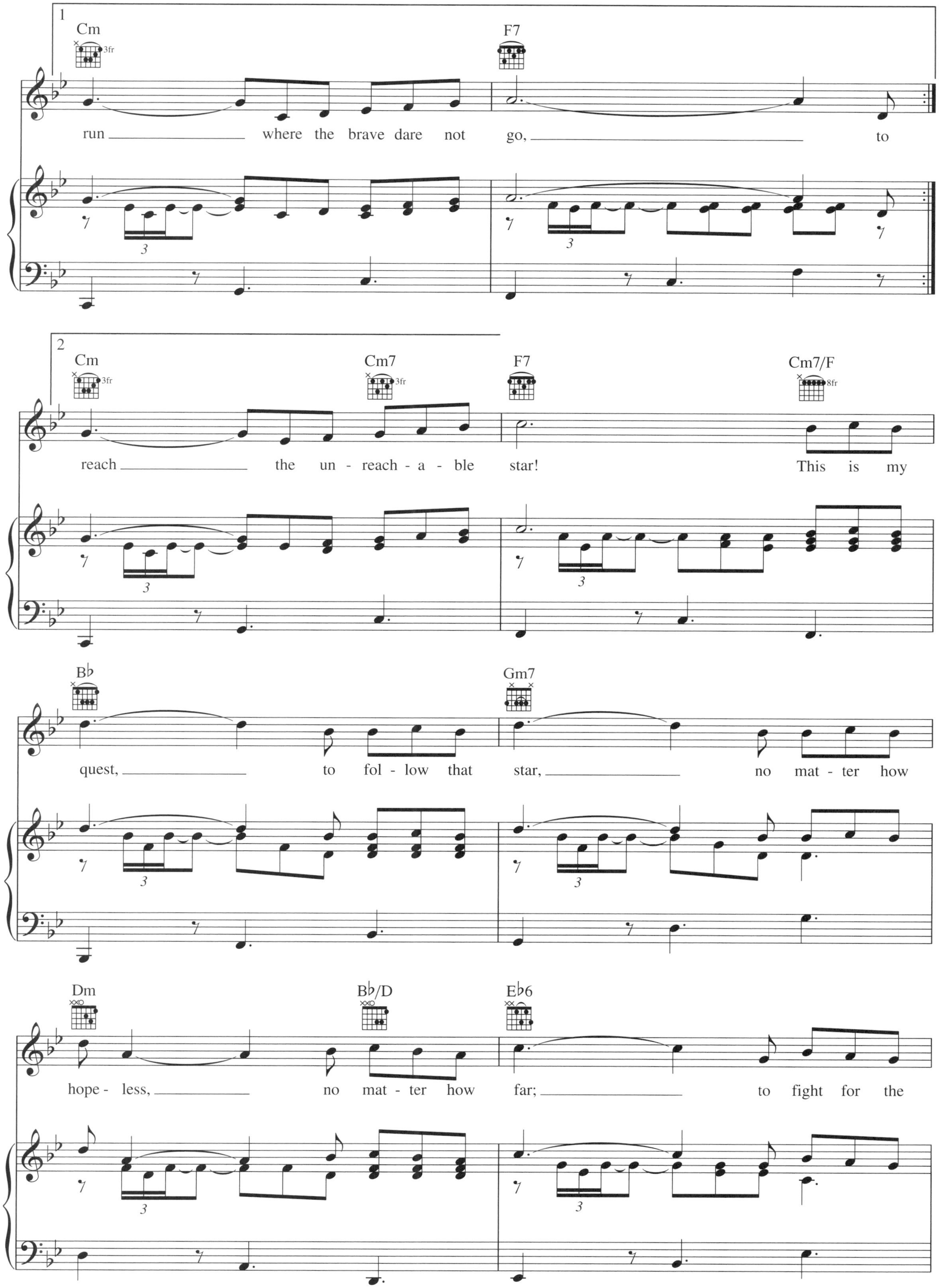
1
Cm
3fr
F7
run ___ where the brave dare not go, ___ to
2
Cm
3fr
Cm7
3fr
F7
Cm7/F
8fr
reach ___ the un - reach - a - ble star! This is my
B♭
Gm7
quest, ___ to fol - low that star, ___ no mat - ter how
Dm
B♭/D
E♭6
hope - less, ___ no mat - ter how far; ___ to fight for the

Gm
G♭
G♭+
right with - out ques - tion or pause, to be will - ing to
B♭/F
G♭+
Gm
A♭
Cm
march in - to hell for a heav - en - ly cause! And I know, if I'll on - ly be
A♭
D
true to this glo - ri - ous quest, that my
E♭6
A7
heart will lie peace - ful and calm, when I'm laid to my

E♭m
F7
B♭(add2)
B♭
B♭(add2)
B♭
rest. And the world will be bet-ter for this, that one
mf
E♭maj7
E♭maj7
E♭6
man, scorned and cov-ered with scars, still
Dm
Dm7
Cm7
strove with his last ounce of cour-age, to
B♭/F
Cm7/F
B♭
reach the un-reach-a-ble stars.
rall.
a tempo

IT MIGHT AS WELL BE SPRING

from STATE FAIR

Lyrics by OSCAR HAMMERSTEIN II
Music by RICHARD RODGERS

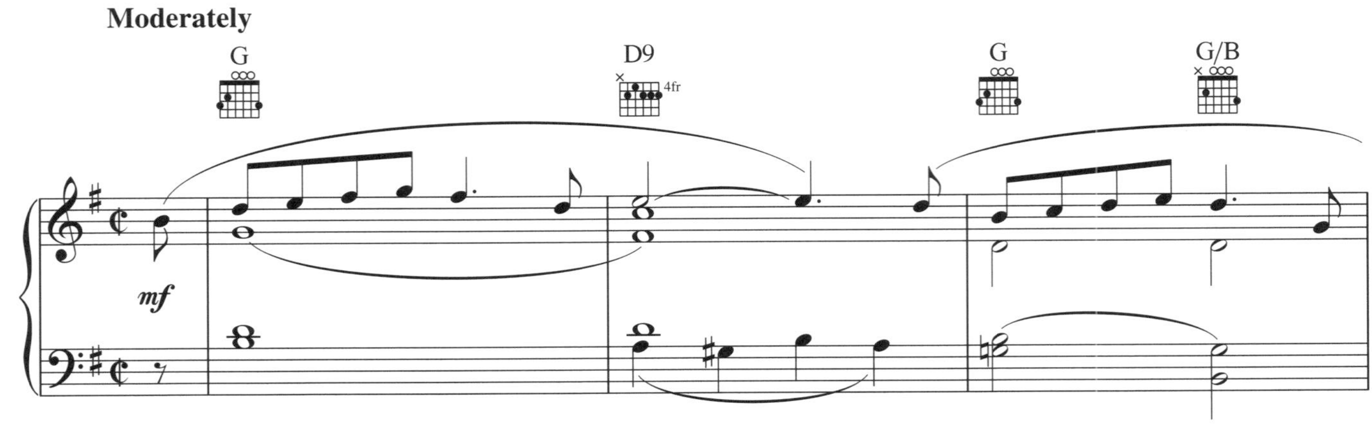

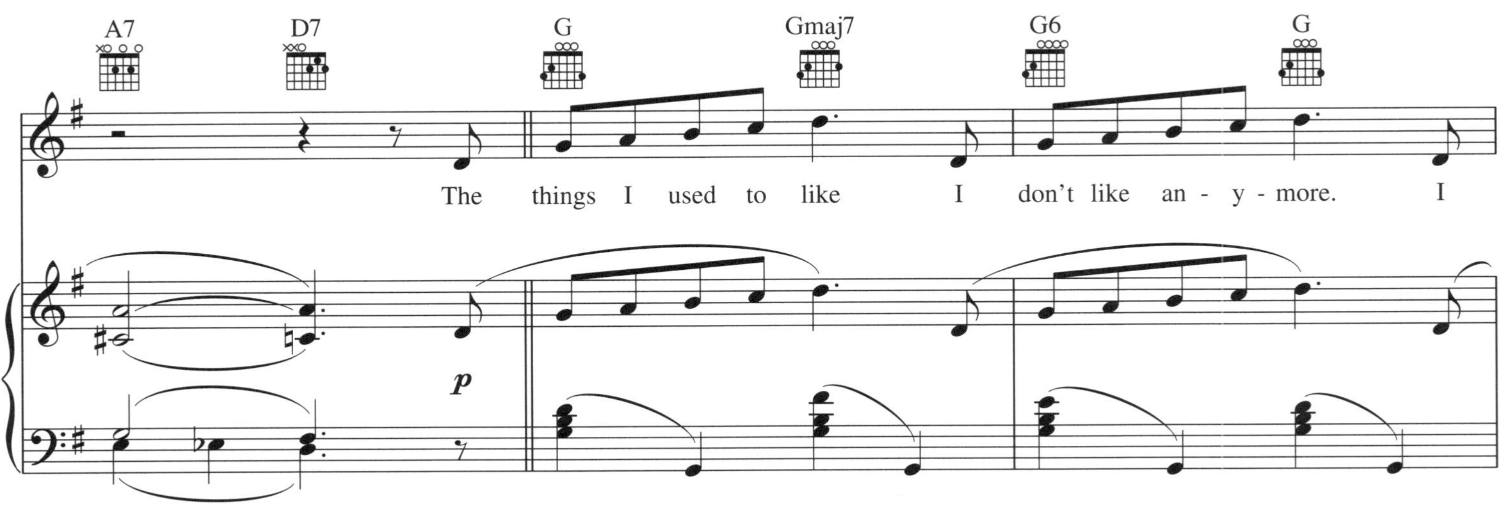

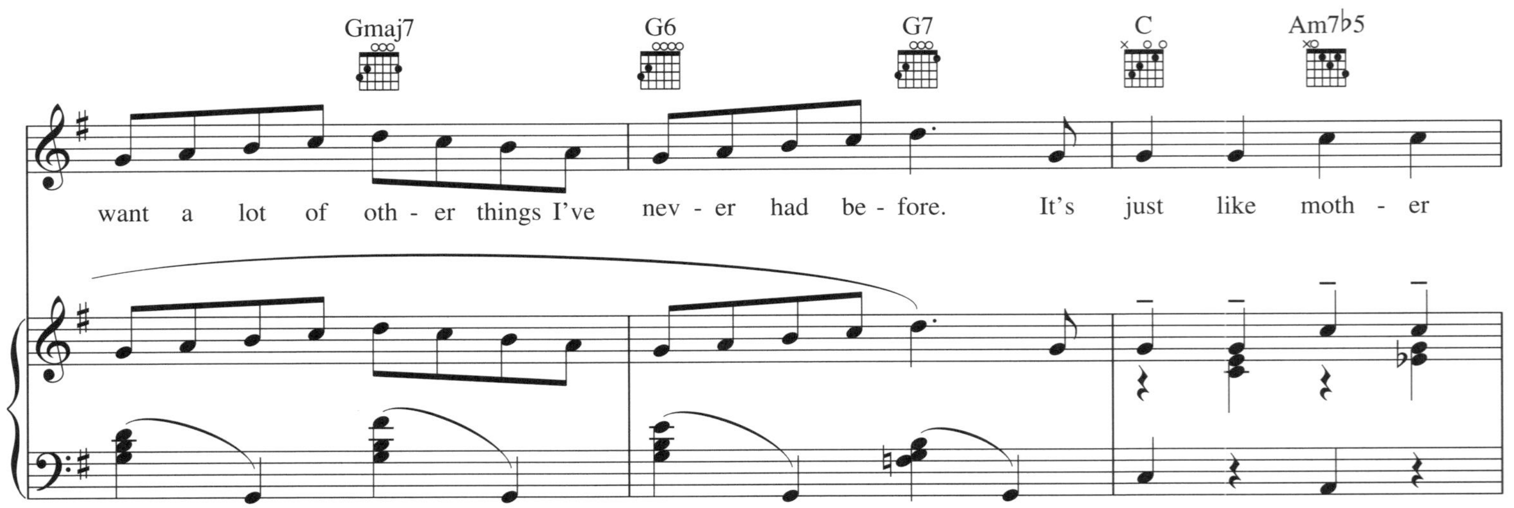

G/D
Am7
D7
G6
G
says, I "sit a - round and mope" Pre -
C
Am7♭5
G/D
Am7
D7
tend - ing I am won - der - ful and know - ing I'm a
G6
G
G6
G
Refrain (gracefully)
G
Gmaj7
dope. I'm as rest - less as a wil - low in a
p - mf
G
Gmaj7
Dm7
G7
wind - storm, I'm as jump - y as a pup - pet on a string. I'd

C
Cdim7
G/B
G/D
Am7
D7
say that I had spring fe - ver, But I know it is - n't
Gmaj7
G6
G
Gmaj7
G
spring. I am star - ry - eyed and vague - ly dis - con - tent - ed, Like a
Gmaj7
Dm7
G7
C
Cdim7
night - in - gale with - out a song to sing. Oh, why should I have spring
G/B
G/D
Am7
D7
G
C
fe - ver When it is - n't e - ven spring? I keep wish - ing I were

Dm7
Dm7/G
Dm7
G7♭5(♯9)
G7
C
some - where else, walk - ing down a strange new street,
F♯m7
B7
Em/G
A7
G
D7
G
D7
Hear - ing words that I have nev - er heard from a {man / girl} I've yet to meet. I'm as
cresc.
mf
p
G
Gmaj7
G
Gmaj7
bus - y as a spi - der spin - ning day - dreams, I'm as gid - dy as a ba - by on a
Dm7
G7
C
Cdim7
G/B
G/D
swing. I haven't seen a cro - cus or a rose - bud, or a

C6
D9
4fr
B7
E7♭9
A7
rob - in on the wing,
But I feel so gay in a
D9
4fr
G7
A7
mel - an - cho - ly way that it might as well be spring.
It
G/D
D7sus
D7
1
G
Em
might as well be spring!
mf
C
D7
2
G
C6
G
I'm as spring!
mf

THE LAST NIGHT OF THE WORLD

from MISS SAIGON

Music by CLAUDE-MICHEL SCHÖNBERG
Lyrics by RICHARD MALTBY JR. and ALAIN BOUBLIL
Adapted from original French Lyrics by ALAIN BOUBLIL

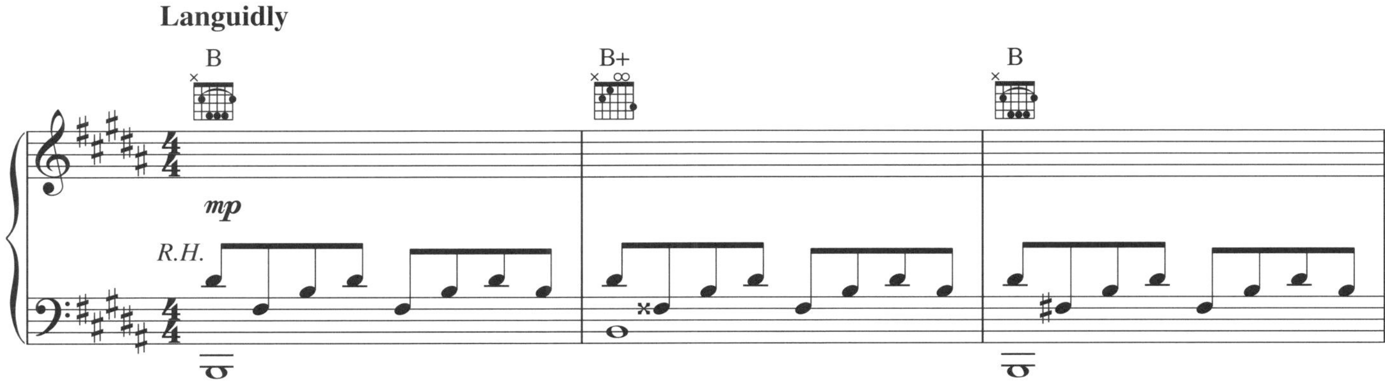

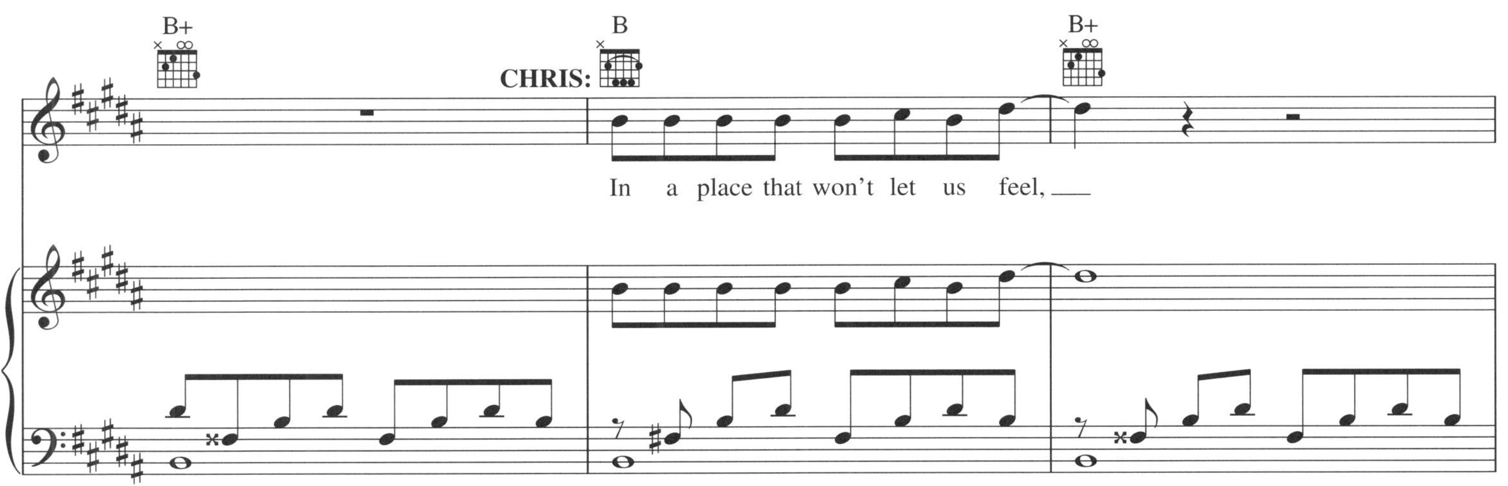

E/F♯
B
B+
I have found you.
B
B+
B
KIM:
In a world that's mov-ing too fast,
in a world where noth-ing can last,
B+
Emaj7
E/F♯
I will hold you,
I will hold
B
C♯m
C♯m/B
CHRIS:
you.
Our lives will change when to-mor-row comes.
KIM:
To-night our

A
CHRIS:
hearts dream the dis - tant drums.
And we have
D
F♯
B
mu - sic al - right
tear - ing the night.
A song
rit.
a tempo
Cdim7
C♯m7
F♯7
4fr
3
played on a so - lo sax - o - phone.
A
B
Cdim7
C♯m
CHRIS:
KIM:
cra - zy sound,
a lone - ly sound,
a cry that tells us love

F♯7
B
Cdim7
goes on and on.
Played on a
C♯m7
F♯
B
so - lo sax - o - phone,
it's tell - ing me to
Cdim7
C♯m7
4fr
F♯7
hold you tight and dance like it's the last night of the
B
B+
B
CHRIS:
world.
On the oth - er side of the earth
R.H.

B+
B
B+
there's a place where life still has worth.
I will
Emaj7
E/F♯
B
KIM:
CHRIS:
take you.
I'll go with you.
You won't be -
C♯m
4fr
C♯m/B
A
lieve all the things you'll see.
I know 'cause you'll see them all with me.
D
F♯
CHRIS:
KIM:
3
If we're to - geth - er, well then, we'll hear it a - gain, a
rit.

B
Cdim7
C♯m7
4fr
song
played on a so - lo sax - o - phone,
a tempo
F♯7
B
Cdim7
A cra - zy sound, a lone - ly sound, a
C♯m
4fr
F♯7
B
cry that tells us love goes on and on.
Cdim7
C♯m
4fr
F♯7
Played on a so - lo sax - o - phone. It's

B
G♯7
C♯m
4fr
4fr
tell - ing me to hold you tight and dance like it's the last
F♯
B
G♯m
4fr
3
KIM:
night of the world.
Dreams were all I
D♯m
6fr
G♯m
4fr
D♯m
6fr
CHRIS:
ev - er knew.
Dreams you won't need when I'm through.
E
B/D♯
4fr
A
BOTH:
CHRIS:
An - y - where we may be
KIM:
I will sing with

Maestoso
F♯
A
D
D♯dim7
you our song.
Em
A7
CHRIS:
D/A
KIM:
So stay with me and
B7/A
Em/A
hold me tight and dance like it's the
A7♭9
5fr
A7
D
Em/D
last night of the world.

D
Gm/B♭
D
Em/D
D
Gm/B♭
D
Gm/B♭
rall.
D

THE JOINT IS JUMPIN'

from AIN'T MISBEHAVIN'

Words by ANDY RAZAF and J.C. JOHNSON
Music by THOMAS "FATS" WALLER

F
C7
F
F♯dim
Gm7
C7
F7
ev - 'ry - thing is in full swing_ when you hear some - bod - y shout: (Here 'tis)
B♭
Bdim
Cm7
F7
B♭
Bdim
Cm7
F7
This joint is jump - in', it's real - ly jump - in'.
This joint is jump - in', it's real - ly jump - in'.
B♭
B♭7
E♭
Edim
B♭
F7
B♭
Come in cats_ an' check_ your hats,_ I mean_ this joint_ is jump - in'.
Ev - 'ry Mose_ is on ___ his toes,_ I mean_ the joint_ is jump - in'.
D
A7
D
A7
D
A7
D
C7
The pi - an - o's thump - in', the danc - ers bump - in'.
No time for talk - in', it's time_ for walk - in'. (Yes!)

F
C7
F
F#dim
C7
F7
This here spot_ is more than hot,_ in fact the joint is jump - in'.
Grab a jug_ and cut the rug,_ I mean this joint is jump - in'.
Bb7
Edim
Bb7
Eb
Bb7
Eb
Check your weap - ons at the door,_ be sure to pay your quar - ter.
Get your pig feet, beer and gin,_ there's plen - ty in the kitch - en.
C7
F9
C7+5
F7
Burn your leath - er on the floor,_ grab an - y - bod - y's daugh - ter.
Who is that that just came in?_ Just look at the way he's switch - in'.
Bb
Bdim
Cm7
F7
Bb
Bdim
Cm7
F7
The roof is rock - in', the neigh-bor's knock - in'.
Don't mind the hour,_ 'cause I'm in pow - er.

Bb
Bb7
Eb
Edim
1.
F7
We're all bums_ when the wag-on comes._ I mean_ this joint is jump - in'. Let it beat!
I got bail_ if we go to jail._ I mean_
2.
F+
Bdim
Cm7
F9
— this joint is jump - in'. This joint is jump - in', It's real-ly jump-
Ebm
in. We're all bums_ when the wag-on comes,_ I mean_ this joint is jump-
Bb+
Gm7
C7
in'. Don't give your right name. No, No, No!

JUNE IS BUSTIN' OUT ALL OVER

from CAROUSEL

Lyrics by OSCAR HAMMERSTEIN II
Music by RICHARD RODGERS

Em E Em E B+/E♭ Bm/D D♭7 Am/C E/B B7♯5
crowd of doubt - in' Thom - as - es Was pre - dict - in' that the Sum - mer'd nev - er
E A/E
MEN:
come. But it's com - in' by gum, y' ken feel it come! Y' ken
mp
D Am7/D
GIRLS:
feel it in your heart, y' ken see it in the ground. Y' ken hear it in the trees, Y' ken
D7 N.C.
ALL:
smell it in the breeze. Look a - round, look a - round, look a - round!
8va
f
sf

Refrain (brightly)
G G6 Gmaj7 G6 Gmaj9
June is bust - in' out all o - ver! All o - ver the
June is bust - in' out all o - ver! The sap - lin's are
June is bust - in' out all o - ver! The o - cean is
mf
G6 F♯dim7 Em Em/D♯
mead - ow and the hill! Buds 're bust - in' out - a
bust - in' out with sap! Love has found my broth - er,
full of Jacks and Jills. With her lit - tle tail a -
Em/D Em/C♯ C Em/B C/B♭ A7 D/F♯ Dm/F
bush - es And the romp - in' riv - er push - es Ev - 'ry lit - tle wheel that
jun - ior, And my sis - ter's e - ven lu - nier! And my ma is get - tin'
swish - in' Ev - 'ry la - dy fish is wish - in' That a male would come and

A7sus
A7
D
D7
G
G6
ALL:
wheels be - side a mill!
kit - ten - ish with pap!
grab her by the gills!
June is bust - in' out all
June is bust - in' out all
June is bust - in' out all
f
mf
Gmaj7
G6
Gmaj9
G6
NETTIE:
o - ver! The feel - in' is get - tin' so in -
o - ver! To la - dies the men are pay - in'
o - ver! The sheep are - n't sleep - in' an - y -
F♯dim7
Em
Em/D♯
Em/D
Em/C♯
tense, That the young Vir - gin - ia creep - ers Hev been
court. Lots - a ships are kept at an - chor Jest be -
more! All the rams that chase the ewe sheep Are de -

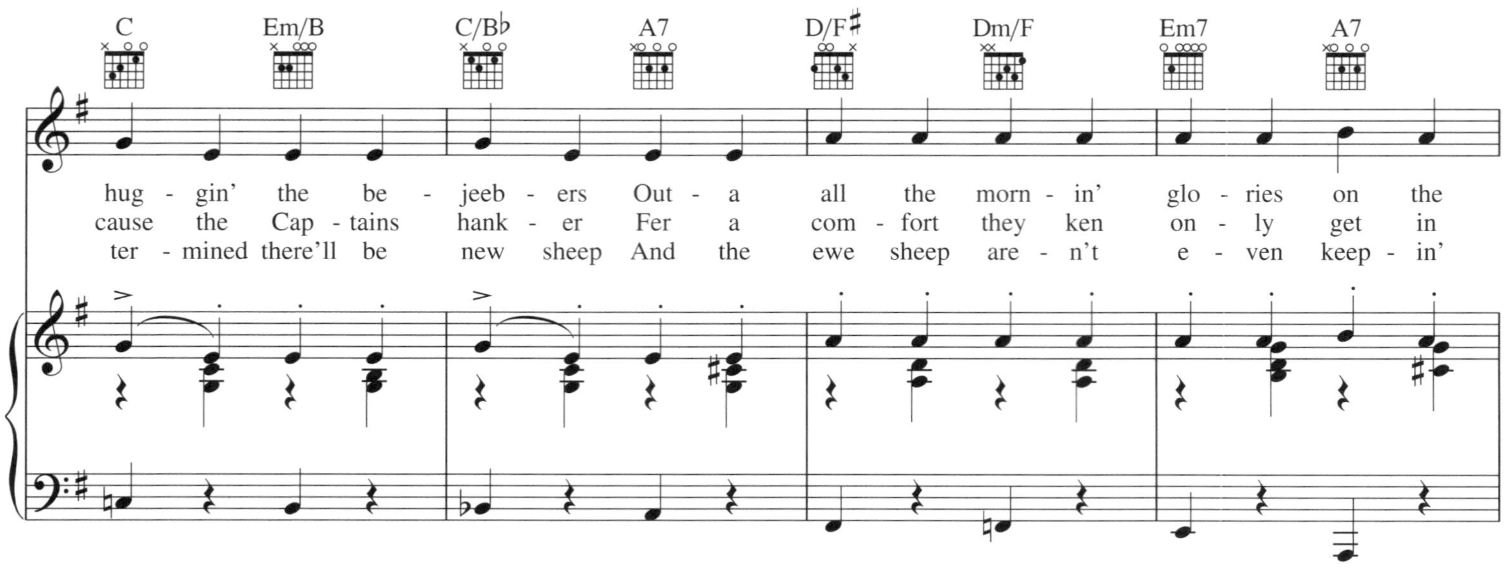
C
Em/B
C/B♭
A7
D/F♯
Dm/F
Em7
A7
hug - gin' the be - jeeb - ers Out - a all the morn - in' glo - ries on the
cause the Cap - tains hank - er Fer a com - fort they ken on - ly get in
ter - mined there'll be new sheep And the ewe sheep are - n't e - ven keep - in'

D
Cmaj9/D
5fr
D7
Gmaj9
G6
Gmaj9
MEN:
fence! Be - cause it's June! June, June,
port! Be - cause it's June! June, June,
score! On a - count - a it's June! June, June,

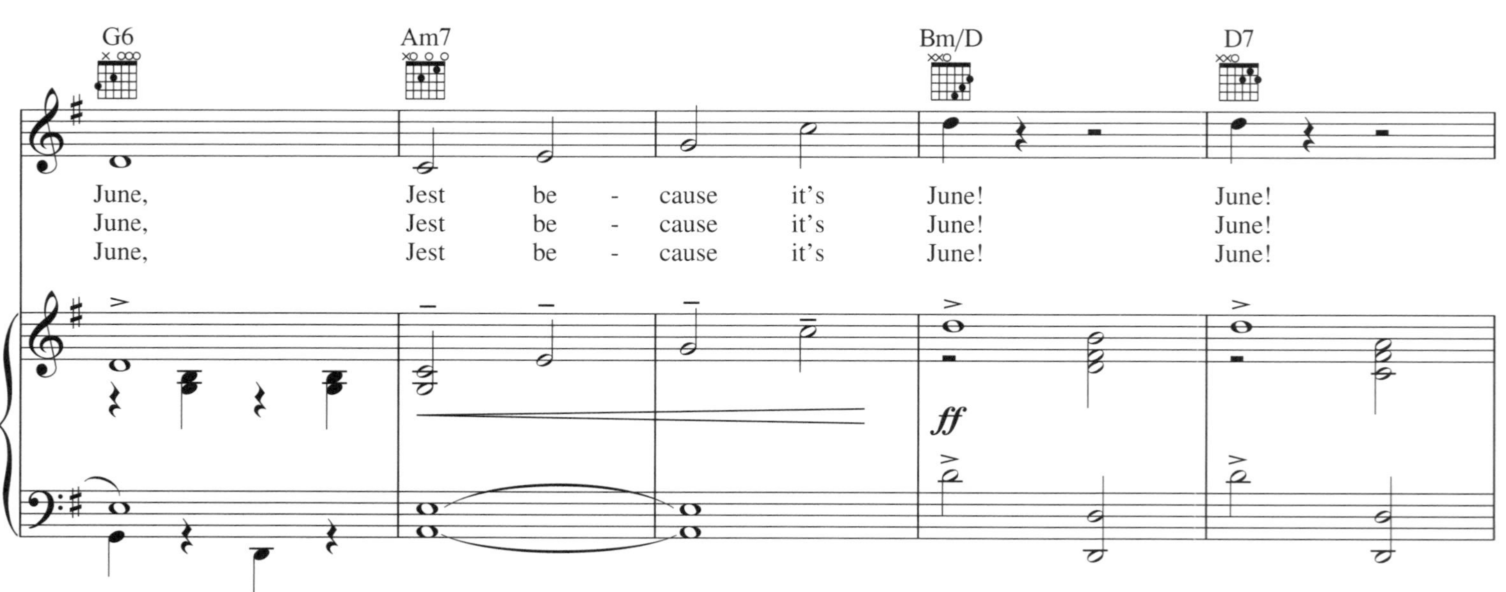
G6
Am7
Bm/D
D7
June, Jest be - cause it's June! June!
June, Jest be - cause it's June! June!
June, Jest be - cause it's June! June!

1, 2
Gmaj9
G6
Gmaj9
G6
rit.
June!
June!
f
rit.
Am7
Eb7
B6/Eb
4fr
D7
NETTIE:
rit.
Fresh and a - live and gay and young, June is a love song sweet - ly sung.
June makes the bay look bright and new, Sails gleam - in' white on sun - lit blue.
rit.
3
Gmaj9
G6
Gmaj9
G6
June!
F6
A13
5fr
D
sf

KISS OF THE SPIDER WOMAN

from KISS OF THE SPIDER WOMAN

Words by FRED EBB
Music by JOHN KANDER

C♯min
G♯7
C♯min
G♯7
bed - room, the par - lor or e - ven the street. There's
C♯min
F♯
C♯min
F♯
no place on earth You're like - ly to miss Her
G♯7sus
G♯7
kiss.
cresc.
C♯min
C♯sus
C♯min
C♯sus(9)
Soon - er or lat - er in sun - light or gloom When the
mp

C♯min
C♯sus
C♯min
C♯sus(9)
red can - dles flick - er she'll walk in the room And the
C♯min
F♯
C♯min
F♯
cur-tain will shake And the fi - re will hiss. Here comes her
G♯7sus
G♯9
kiss. And the
cresc.
rall. poco a poco
A tempo
C♯min
C♯min/B
D♯7/A♯
F♯min/A
G♯7
moon grows dim - mer At the
f
marc.

C♯min
C♯min/B
D♯7/A♯
tide's low ebb And her
F♯min(6)/A
G♯7
C♯min
C♯min/B
black beads shim - mer And you're
D♯7/A♯
F♯min(6)/A
G♯7sus
G♯7
ach - ing to move But you're caught in the web Of the
rall.
C♯min
C♯min/B
D♯7/A♯
F♯min/A
G♯7
Spi - der - wom - an With her
a tempo

C♯min
C♯min/B
D♯7/A♯
F♯min(6)/A
vel - vet cape. You can
C♯min/G♯
F♯min C♯min
G♯7sus
G♯7
scream
But you can - not es -
rall. poco a poco
colla voce
A tempo
C♯min(9)
G♯7
C♯min(9)
G♯7
cape.
p
C♯min (♯7)
G♯7
C♯min(9)
G♯7
f

C♯min
G♯7
C♯min
G♯7
Soon - er or lat - er your love will ar - rive And he
mp stacc.
C♯min
G♯7
C♯min
G♯7
touch - es your heart. You're a - lert and a - live. And there's
C♯min
F♯
C♯min
F♯
on - ly one pin That can punc - ture such bliss: Her
G♯7sus
G♯7
kiss.
poco cresc.

C♯min
C♯sus(9)
C♯min
C♯sus(9)
Soon - er or la - ter you bathe in suc - cess And your
f
mp
C♯min
C♯sus(9)
C♯min
C♯sus(9)
min - ions sa - lute. They say noth - ing but "yes." But your
C♯min
F♯
C♯min
F♯
pow - er is emp - ty. It fades like the mist Once you've been
G♯7sus
G♯7
kissed. And the
cresc.
rall. poco a poco

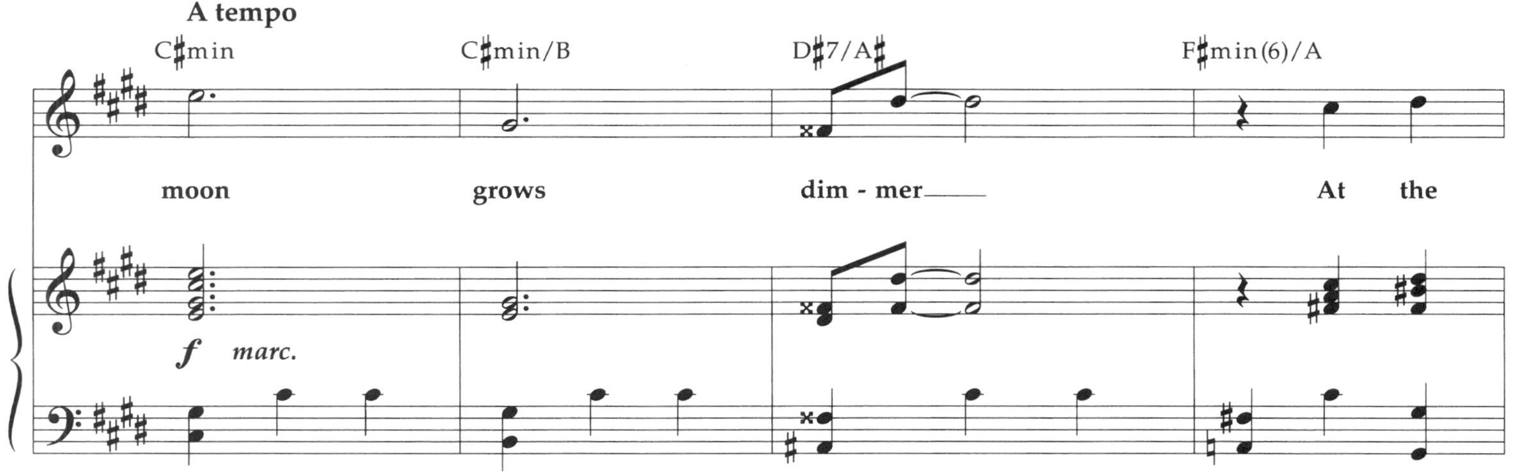
A tempo
C♯min
C♯min/B
D♯7/A♯
F♯min(6)/A
moon grows dim - mer___ At the
f marc.

C♯min
C♯min/B
D♯7/A♯
tide's low ebb. And your

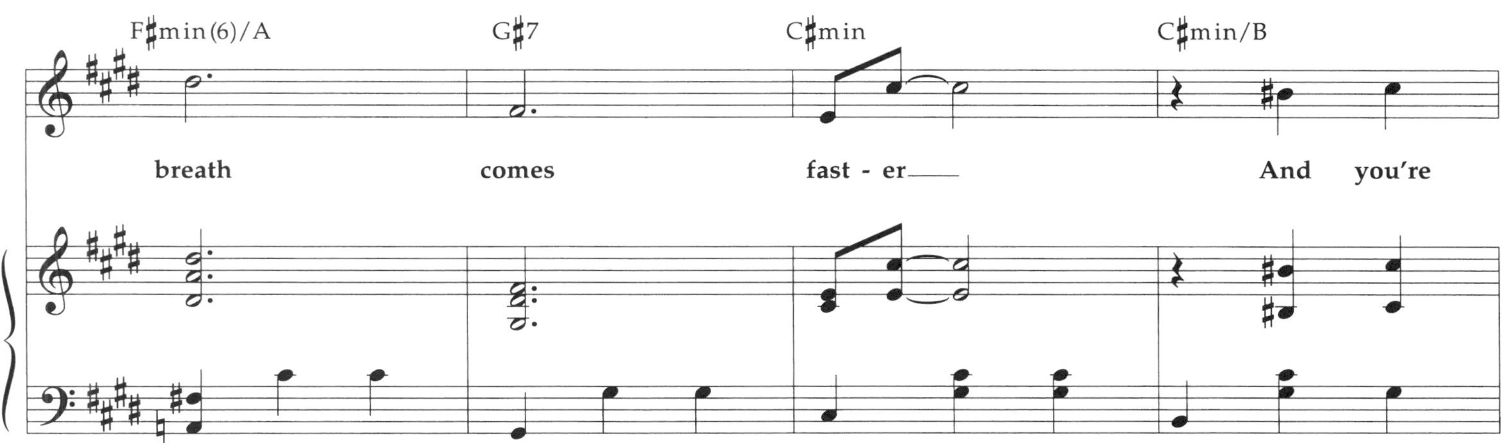
F♯min(6)/A
G♯7
C♯min
C♯min/B
breath comes fast - er___ And you're

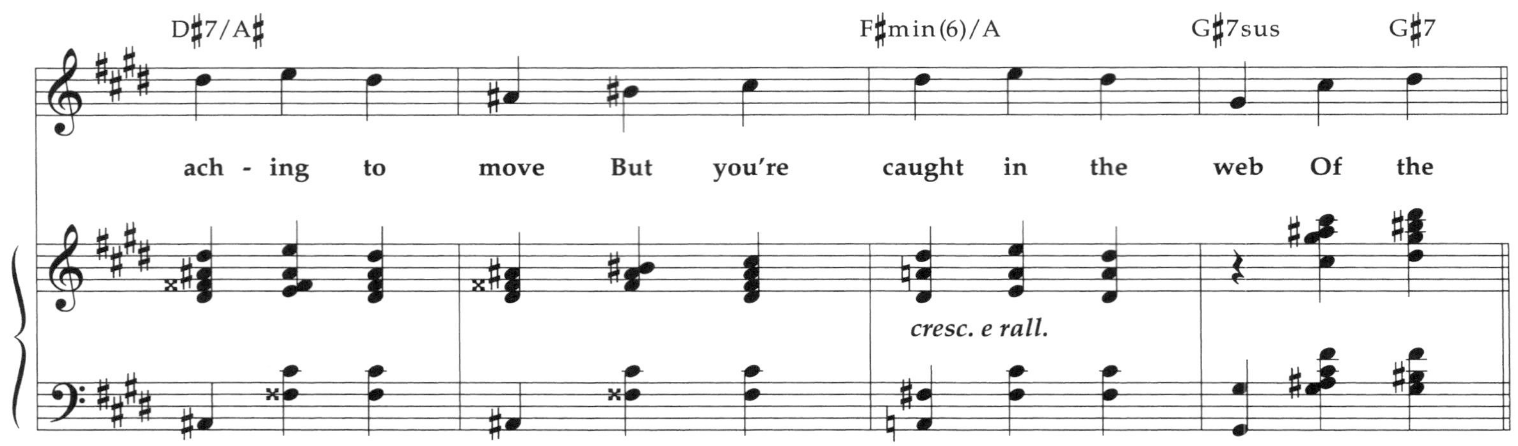
D♯7/A♯
F♯min(6)/A
G♯7sus
G♯7
ach - ing to move But you're caught in the web Of the
cresc. e rall.

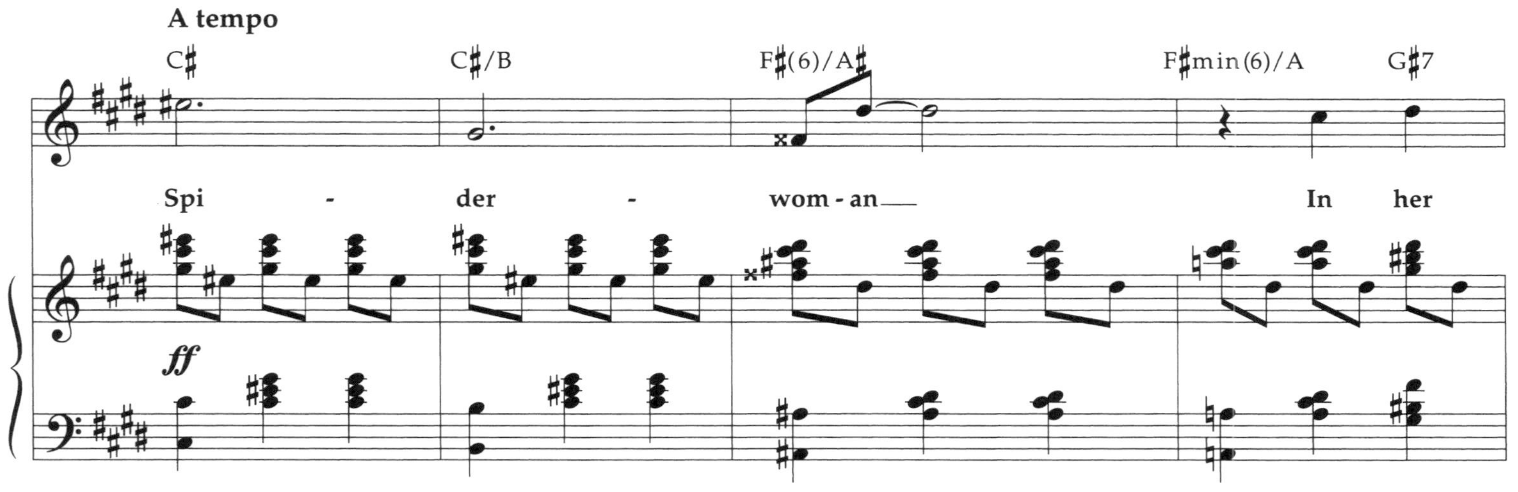
A tempo
C♯
C♯/B
F♯(6)/A♯
F♯min(6)/A
G♯7
Spi - der - wom - an In her
ff

C♯
C♯/B
F♯/A♯
F♯min/A
vel - - vet cape. You can
rall.

C♯min/G♯
G♯7
run,
You can
scream,
You can
cresc. poco a poco
Maestoso
E/G♯
G♯7sus(♭9)
hide,
But you
can - not es -
A tempo
C♯min(9)
C♯sus(♭9)
C♯min(9)
C♯sus(♭9)
cape.
ff
C♯min(9)
C♯sus(♭9)
C♯min
sfz

THE LADY IS A TRAMP

from BABES IN ARMS

Words by LORENZ HART
Music by RICHARD RODGERS

C9
F
Fm6
both - er with peo - ple I hate,
C
C+
F6
G9
9fr
C
G7
That's why the la - dy is a tramp.
mf
C
Cm7
3fr
Dm7
G7
I don't like crap - games with Bar - ons and Earls,
C
Cm7
3fr
Dm7
G7
Won't go to Har - lem in er - mine and pearls.

C Cmaj7 C9 F Fm6
Won't dish the dirt with the rest of the girls,
C C+ F G7 C
That's why the la - dy is a tramp.
N.C.
I like the
Fmaj7 G7 Em7 Am
free fresh wind in my hair,
mf
Dm7 G7 C A7 D7 G7
Life with - out care.
I'm broke,
it's oke.

C
Cm7
3fr
Dm
E7
Hate Cal - i - for - nia, It's cold and it's damp,
p
Am
C+
Am7
1
D7
G7
C
Am
Dm7
G7
That's why the la - dy is a tramp.
mf
2
D7
D7♭5/A♭
G7
C
Cmaj7
la - dy is a tramp.
f
Cm7
3fr
Dm/C
Fm/C
G7
C
sf

LITTLE GIRL BLUE

from JUMBO

Words by LORENZ HART
Music by RICHARD RODGERS

F
B♭maj7
C9
F
F7♭9
Sit there and count the rain - drops fall - ing on you.
p
B♭
Gm7♭5
F/C
D7
G7
It's time you knew, all you can count on is the
C7sus
C7
F
B♭
F
A♭dim7
rain - drops That fall on lit - tle girl blue.
No use, old
mf
mp
C7
F6
girl, you may as well sur - ren - der, Your

A7sus
A7
hope is get - ting slen - der, Why won't some - bod - y
Dm
D7♯5
G7
B♭m/D♭
F/C
A7♯5
send a ten - der Blue boy to
p
B♭maj7
C7
1 F
C7
cheer a lit - tle girl blue?
2, 3 F
Fine
Trio
F
blue?
When I was ver - y
f
p

Gm7
C7
F6
young the world was young - er than
C7
I, As mer - ry as a car - ou -
F6
Gm7
sel. The cir - cus tent was strung
C7
F6
with ev - 'ry star in the sky A -

C7
F6
bove the ring I loved so well.
Dm7
Now the young world has grown
mp
Gm7
F/C
old, Gone are the
C7
D.S. al Fine
tin - sel and gold.

LOOK FOR THE SILVER LINING

from SALLY

Words by BUDDY DeSYLVA
Music by JEROME KERN

Refrain *(slowly, with warm expression)*

E♭
B♭7
E♭
E♭7
heart full of joy and glad - ness will al - ways ban - ish
A♭maj7
A♭6
F7
sad - ness and strife. So al - ways look for the sil - ver
E♭
A♭m6
B♭7
lin - ing, and try to find the sun - ny side of
1
E♭
B♭7
Fm7
B♭7
life.
2
E♭
life.

LOVE CHANGES EVERYTHING

from ASPECTS OF LOVE

Music by ANDREW LLOYD WEBBER
Lyrics by DON BLACK and CHARLES HART

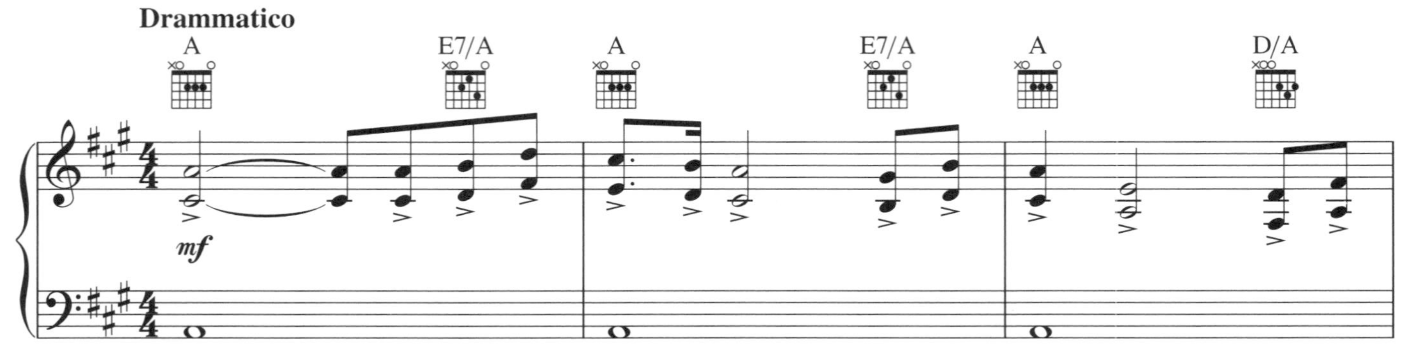

A E7 A D A
ev - 'ry - thing: how you live and how you die.
strong - est heart, pain is deep - er than be - fore.
E7 A A/C♯ D
Love can make the sum - mer fly or a night seem like a
Love will turn your world a - round and that world will last for -
A/E E7 A E7 A E7
life - time. Yes love, love chang - es ev - 'ry - thing: now I
ev - er. Yes love, love chang - es ev - 'ry - thing; brings you
A E A D
trem - ble at your name. Noth - ing in the world will ev - er
glo - ry, brings you shame. Noth - ing in the world will ev - er
cresc.

D/E
E7
1
A
D/A
A
be the same.
be the
2
A
A/G
D/F♯
same.
cresc.
ff
Bm7
A/E
Esus
E
B♭
F
B♭
F
B♭
E♭
3fr
Off into the world we go, plan-ning fu-tures, shap-ing
f

B♭ E♭/B♭ B♭ F B♭ F
6fr
years. Love bursts in and sud - den - ly, all our
B♭ E♭ B♭ F F7
3fr
wis - dom dis - ap - pears. Love makes fools of
poco ritard
a tempo
B♭ E♭ B♭/F F F7
3fr
ev - ery - one: all the rules we make are bro - ken. Yes
B♭ F B♭ F B♭ F
love, love chang - es ev - 'ry - thing. Live or per - ish in its

B♭
E♭
3fr
E♭/F
F7
flame.
Love will nev - er, nev - er let you be the
cresc.
poco ritard
ff a tempo
B♭
B♭/A♭
E♭/G
same.
Love will nev - er, nev - er let you
cresc.
fff
E♭/F
F7
B♭
F7/B♭
B♭
F7/B♭
be the same.
rall.
a tempo, meno mosso
dim.
B♭
E♭/F
B♭
molto rall.
f
cresc.

LUCK BE A LADY

from GUYS AND DOLLS

By FRANK LOESSER

F6
F♯dim7
C/G
F9
B9
yet be - fore this eve - ning is o - ver, you might give me the brush. _ You
E
C7
E
A♭
C/G
Dm7
G7
might for - get your man - ners, you might re - fuse to stay, and so the best that I can do is
Brightly, in 2
C
D♭7
C
D♭7
pray.
C
D♭7
C
D♭7
Luck be a la - dy to - night.

C
Db7
Luck be a la - dy to - night.
Luck if you've ev - er been a la - dy to be - gin with,
luck be a la - dy to - night.
Ab7
Db
D7
Luck, let a gen - tle - man see

D♭
D7
how nice a dame you can be.
I know they say you've treat - ed
oth - er guys you've been with.
Luck be a la - dy with me.
A7
A

D
A7♭9
5fr
D
la - dy does - n't leave her es - cort. It is - n't
Am6/C
Bm7
E7
E7♭9
fair, it is - n't nice! A
Am
la - dy does - n't wan - der all ov - ver the
B7♭9
Em
B7/D♯
room and blow on some oth - er guy's

G9/D
9fr
G7sus
G7
C
dice.
So let's keep the
Db7
4fr
C
Db7
par - ty po - lite.
C
Db7
C
Db7
Nev - er get out of my sight.
C
Db7
C
Db7
Stick with me ba - by, I'm the fel - low you came in with,

C
Db7
4fr
Luck be a la - dy, luck be a
la - dy, luck be a la - dy to - night.
ff

MAKE BELIEVE

from SHOW BOAT

Lyrics by OSCAR HAMMERSTEIN II
Music by JEROME KERN

Cmaj7
C7
And if the things we dream a - bout don't hap - pen to be
F
Dm7♭5
C/G
Dm/G
so, that's just an un - im - por - tant
G7
C
C♯dim7
tech - ni - cal - i - ty. We could
Slower
G7
make be - lieve I love you, on - ly

C
Em7
E♭dim7
make be - lieve that you love me. Oth - ers
3
G7/D
Dm7/C
G/B
F/A
G7
find peace of mind in pre - tend - ing. Could - n't
C/E
D7
G7
C♯dim7
you? Could - n't I? Could - n't we make be -
G7
lieve our lips are blend - ing in a

C
D7
phan - tom kiss,
or two or
three?
Might as
F6
F♯dim7
C/G
C♯dim7
well make be - lieve I love you,
for, to
G7
1
C
C♯dim7
tell the truth,
I
do.
We could
2
C
Alternate Ending
C
do.
do.
Your par-don I

Dm7 G7 Cmaj7 C6

pray, 'twas too much to say the words that be -

Bm7♭5 G7 Em7 C/E

tray my heart. We on - ly pre -

G7 C6

tend, you do not of - fend in play-ing a

Dm7 G7 C

lov - er's part.

rall.

MEMORY

from CATS

Music by ANDREW LLOYD WEBBER
Text by TREVOR NUNN after T.S. ELIOT

Cm
Gm
lamp - light the with-ered leaves col - lect at my feet and the
mem - ber the time I knew what hap - pi - ness was, let the
1
F
E♭/F
B♭
wind be - gins to moan.
2
F
E♭/F
B♭
mem - ory live a - gain.
Dm
Dm/E♭
Cm/E♭
Dm
Dm/E♭
Cm/E♭
Ev - 'ry street lamp seems to beat a
3fr

Dm
B♭maj7
C
F
Fmaj7
fa - tal - is - tic warn - ing.
Dm
Gm7
C7
Fmaj7
Some - one mut - ters and a street lamp gut - ters and
Dm
Dm/G
G7
C
soon it will be morn - ing.
poco rit.
B♭
Gm
3fr
Day - light. I must wait for the sun - rise, I must think of a
a tempo

E♭
3fr
Dm
new life and I must-n't give in. When the
10
8
Cm
3fr
Gm
3fr
dawn comes to-night will be a mem-o-ry too and a
12
8
F
E♭/F
B♭
new day will be-gin.
6
8
G♭
E♭m
6fr

C♭
B♭m
A♭m7
4fr
E♭m
6fr
D♭
C♭/D♭
4fr
G♭
B♭m
B♭m/C♭
A♭m/C♭
4fr
B♭m
B♭m/C♭
A♭m/C♭
4fr
B♭m
G♭
A♭7
4fr
Burnt out ends of smo - ky days, the stale cold smell of

D♭
B♭m7
E♭m7
6fr
morn - ing. The street lamp dies, an - oth - er
A♭7
4fr
D♭maj7
B♭m
E♭7
night is o - ver, an - oth - er day is
A♭
4fr
A♭7
4fr
D♭
dawn - ing. Touch me. It's so eas - y to
poco rit.
a tempo
B♭m
G♭
leave me all a - lone with the mem - ory of my days in the
rall.

Fm
E♭7sus
E♭m
sun. If you touch me you'll un - der - stand what
a tempo
B♭m
A♭
G♭/A♭
hap - pi - ness is. Look a new day has be -
rall.
D♭
gun.
a tempo - slightly slower

MAMA, I'M A BIG GIRL NOW

from HAIRSPRAY

Music by MARC SHAIMAN
Lyrics by MARC SHAIMAN and SCOTT WITTMAN

Freely

F Dm Bb C

Mothers: Stop! *Penny:* Stop tell - ing me what to do - oo. *Mothers:* Don't! *Amber:* Don't treat me like a child of two - oo. *Mothers:* No! *Tracy:* I know that you want what's best. *Mothers:* Please! *Tracy:* But, moth - er, please *Tracy, Amber & Penny:* give it a rest!

sfz sfz sfz sfz

A fun Shuffle (♩♩ = ♩♪ triplet)

f

F
Dm
Mothers: Stop! Don't! No! Girls: Please! Mothers: Stop! Don't!
mf
Bb
No! Girls: Please! Mothers: Stop! Don't! No! Girls: Please!
C
C7
F
C
F
Ma-ma, I'm a big girl now! Tracy: Once up-on a time when I was
f
mp
Dm
just a kid, you nev-er let me do just what the old-er kids did. But

B♭
C
C7
F
lose that laun - dry list of what you won't al - low, 'cause, ma - ma, I'm a big girl now!
C
F
Amber: Once up - on a time I used to play with toys, but
f
mp
Dm
B♭
now I'd rath - er play a - round with teen - age boys. So, if I get a hick - ey, please don't
C
C7
F
F7
have a cow, 'cause, ma - ma, I'm a big girl now!
Penny: Ma,
mf

B♭
F
I got - ta tell you that with - out a doubt I get my best danc - ing les - sons from you -
- oo. You're the one who taught me how to "Twist and Shout" be-cause you
G
Dm/C
C
shout non - stop and you're so twist - ed too - oo! Wo - oh - oh - oh - oh!
f
Dm
Tracy: Once I used to fid - get 'cause I just sat home. Amber: But now I'm just like Gid - get and I
mf

B♭
Tracy:
Amber:
got - ta get to Rome! Penny: So, say ar - ri - ve - der - ci! Too - dle - oo! And ciao! Girls: 'Cause,
C
C7
F
D♭
G♭
ma - ma, I'm a big girl now! All: Oh - oh - oh! Stop! Don't!
f
E♭m
6fr
No! Please! Stop! Don't! No! Please!
C♭
D♭
D♭7
4fr
G♭
Stop! Don't! No! Please! Ma - ma, I'm a big girl now!

Db
Gb
Ebm
Gb7
Cb
Db7
6fr
4fr
Chorus: Hey, ma - ma, say, ma - ma.
Tracy:
Once up - on a time I was a shy young thing. Could
bare - ly walk and talk so much as dance and sing. But let me hit the stage, I wan - na
take my bow, 'cause, ma - ma, I'm a big girl now!
Amber: Wo - oh - oh - oh - oh!
Once up - on a time I used to dress up "Ken," but now that I'm a wom - an I like
mf
f

C♭
D♭
D♭7
G♭
B♭m/A♭
G♭7/B♭
C♭
G♭
C♭
A♭
4fr
6fr
4fr
4fr
big - ger men! And I don't need a Bar - bie doll to show me how, 'cause,
ma - ma, I'm a big girl now! Girls: Ma, you al - ways taught me what was
right from wrong, and now I just wan - na give it a try - y. Ma -
- ma, I've been in the nest for far too long. So please give a push and, ma - ma,
f

E♭m/D♭ D♭ E♭m/D♭ D♭ D
watch me fly! Amber: Watch me fly!
Chorus: Hey, ma - ma, say, ma - ma. Penny: One day I will meet a man you
G
ff
mf
won't con - demn. Amber: And we will have some kids and you can
Em
tor - ture them. Tracy: But let me be a star be - fore I take that vow, Girls: 'cause,
C

D
D7
G
D/F♯
Em
Em/D
C
D7
G
ma - ma, I'm a big girl now!
Oh - oh - oh!
Ma - ma, I'm a big girl now!
D/F♯
Em
Em/D
C6
D7
Amber: Hey - hey - hey - hey - hey!
Girls: Ma - ma, I'm a big girl!
f
G
Amber: Ooh, such a big, big girl! I'm a big girl now!
All: Stop! Don't!

Em
Oh - oh - oh - oh - oh.
No! Please! Stop! Don't!
C
Oh - oh - oh - oh.
No! Please! Stop! Don't!
D
D7
G
Please!
Ma - ma, I'm a big girl now!
No! Please! Ma - ma, I'm a big girl now!
ff

MANHATTAN

from the Broadway Musical THE GARRICK GAIETIES

Words by LORENZ HART
Music by RICHARD RODGERS

C
C/B♭
A7
Dm
Dm7♭5
G7
We'll set - tle down right here in town.

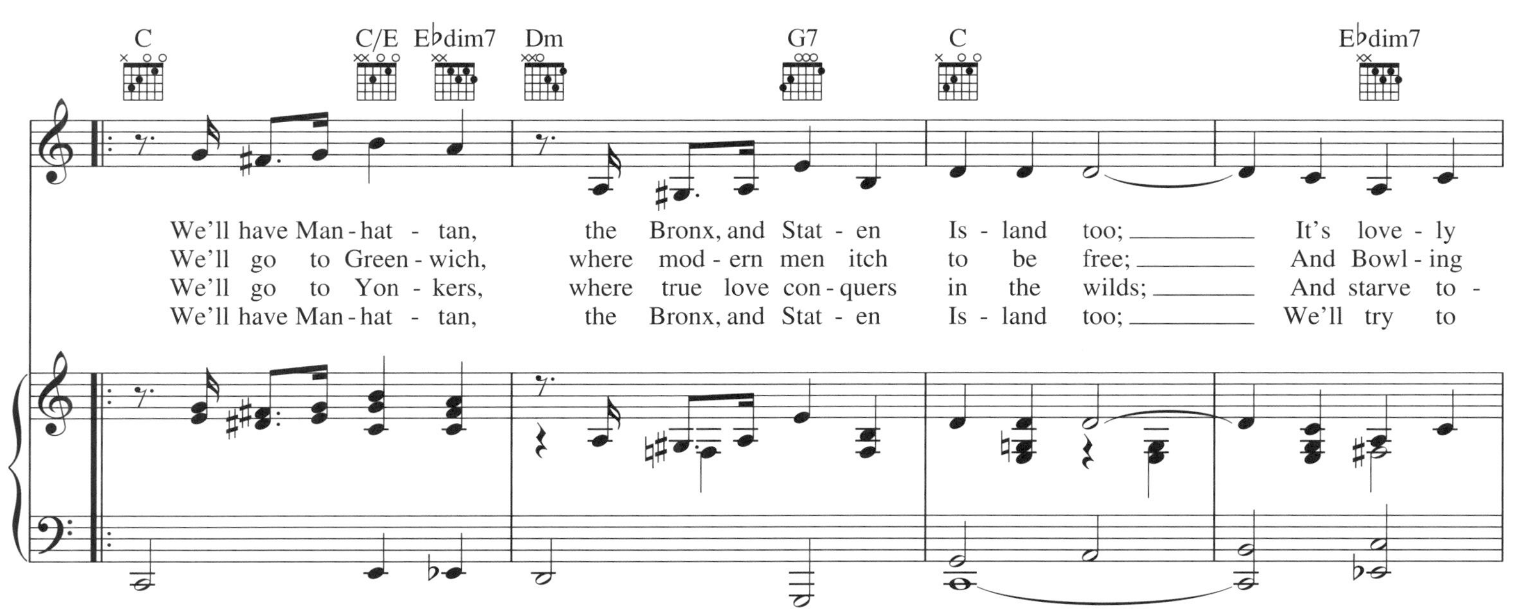
C
C/E
E♭dim7
Dm
G7
C
E♭dim7
We'll have Man - hat - tan, the Bronx, and Stat - en Is - land too; It's love - ly
We'll go to Green - wich, where mod - ern men itch to be free; And Bowl - ing
We'll go to Yon - kers, where true love con - quers in the wilds; And starve to -
We'll have Man - hat - tan, the Bronx, and Stat - en Is - land too; We'll try to

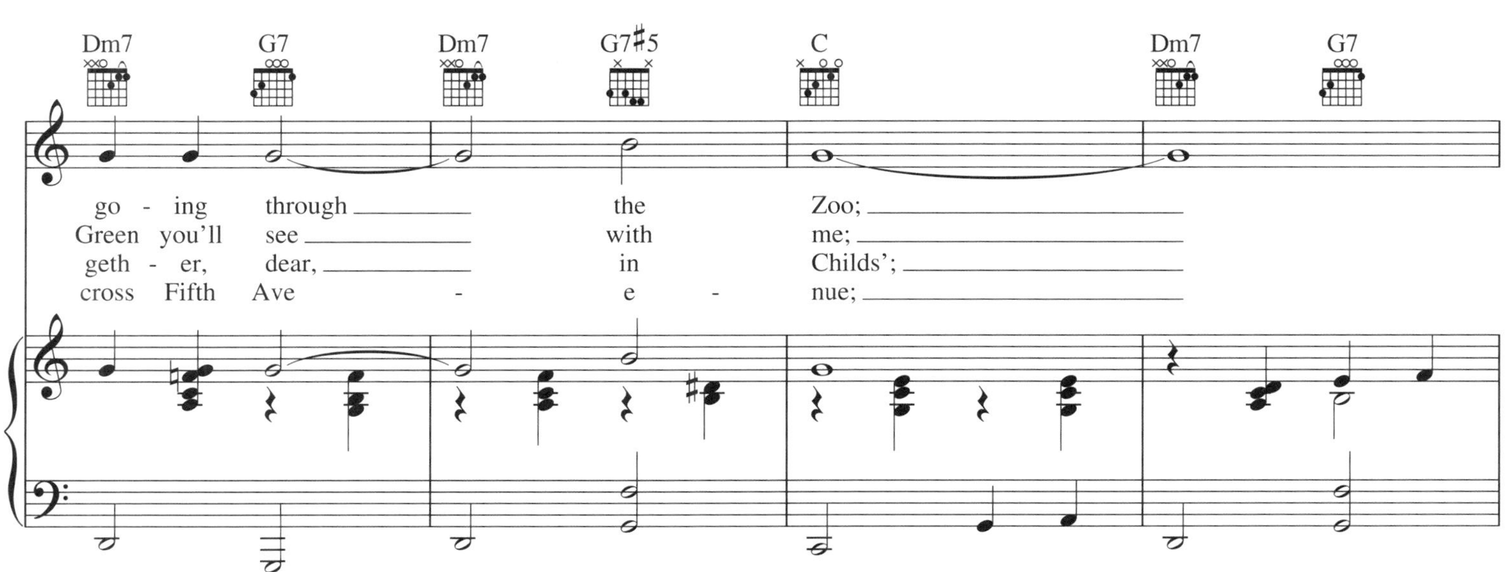
Dm7
G7
Dm7
G7♯5
C
Dm7
G7
go - ing through the Zoo;
Green you'll see with me;
geth - er, dear, in Childs';
cross Fifth Ave - e - nue;

C C/E E♭dim7 Dm G7 G♯dim Am7 Em E♭dim7
3fr
It's ver - y fan - cy on old De - lan - cey Street, you know; The sub - way
We'll bathe at Brigh - ton, the fish you'll fright - en when you're in; Your bath - ing
We'll go to Co - ney and eat bo - lo - gna on a roll; In Cen - tral
As black as on - yx we'll find the Bron - nix Park Ex - press; Our Flat - bush

D7 Dm7 G7 Dm G7 C A7
charms us so, when balm - y breez - es blow to and fro; And tell me what street
suit so thin will make the shell - fish grin fin to fin; I'd like to take a
Park, we'll stroll where our first kiss we stole, soul to soul; Our fu - ture ba - bies
flat, I guess will be a great suc - cess, more or less. A short va - ca - tion

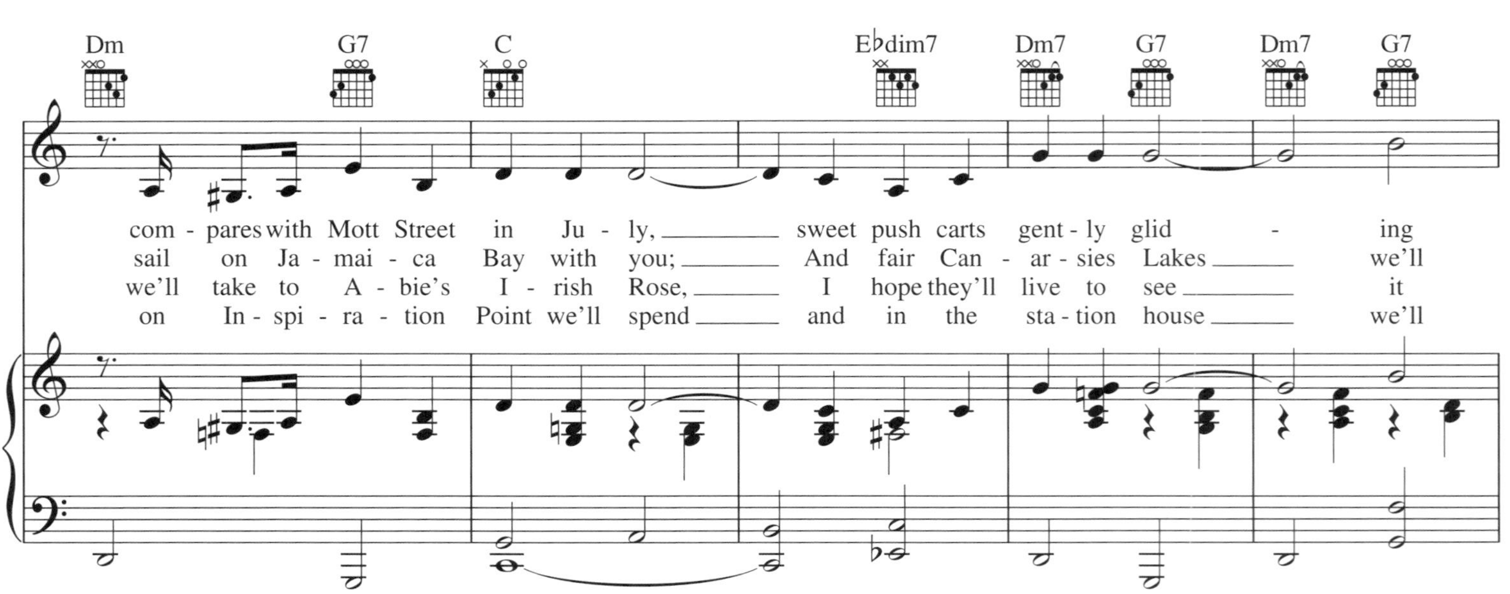
Dm G7 C E♭dim7 Dm7 G7 Dm7 G7
com - pares with Mott Street in Ju - ly, sweet push carts gent - ly glid - ing
sail on Ja - mai - ca Bay with you; And fair Can - ar - sies Lakes we'll
we'll take to A - bie's I - rish Rose, I hope they'll live to see it
on In - spi - ra - tion Point we'll spend and in the sta - tion house we'll

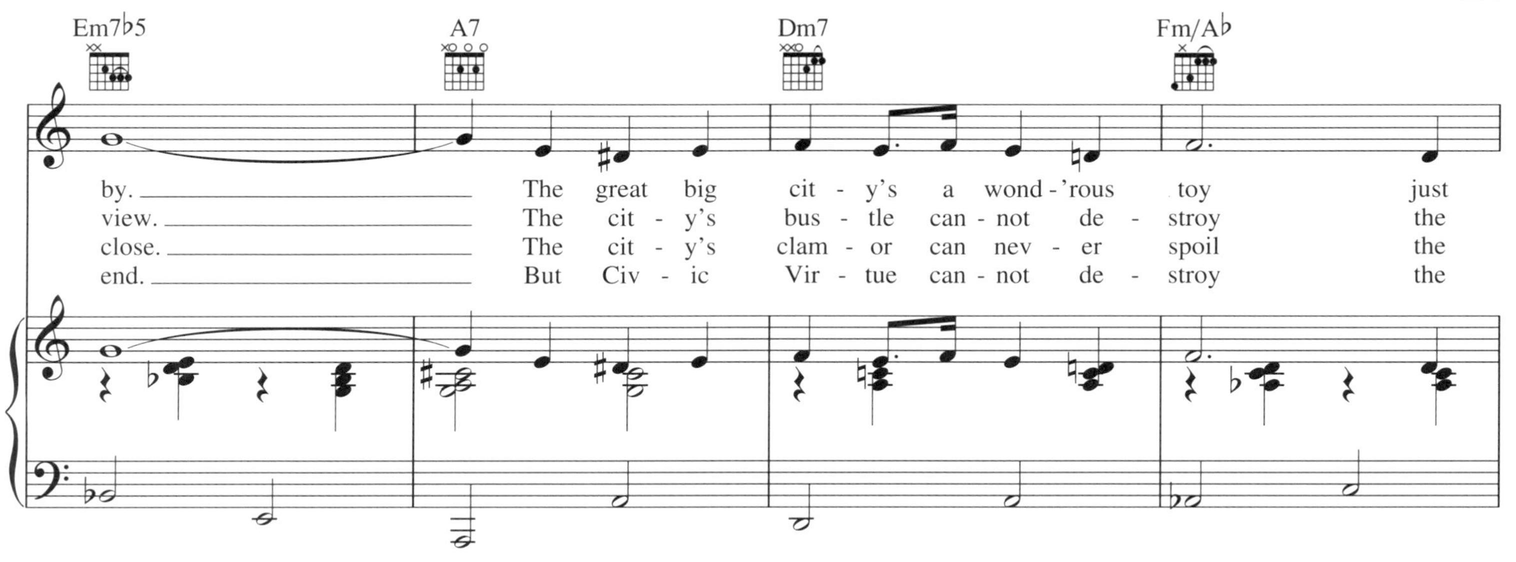
Em7♭5
A7
Dm7
Fm/A♭
by. The great big cit - y's a wond - 'rous toy just
view. The cit - y's bus - tle can - not de - stroy the
close. The cit - y's clam - or can nev - er spoil the
end. But Civ - ic Vir - tue can - not de - stroy the

C/G
D7
C/G
C/E
E♭dim7
D7
G7
made for a girl and boy.
dreams of a girl and boy.
dreams of a boy and goil.
dreams of a girl and boy.
We'll turn Man - hat - tan in - to an isle of

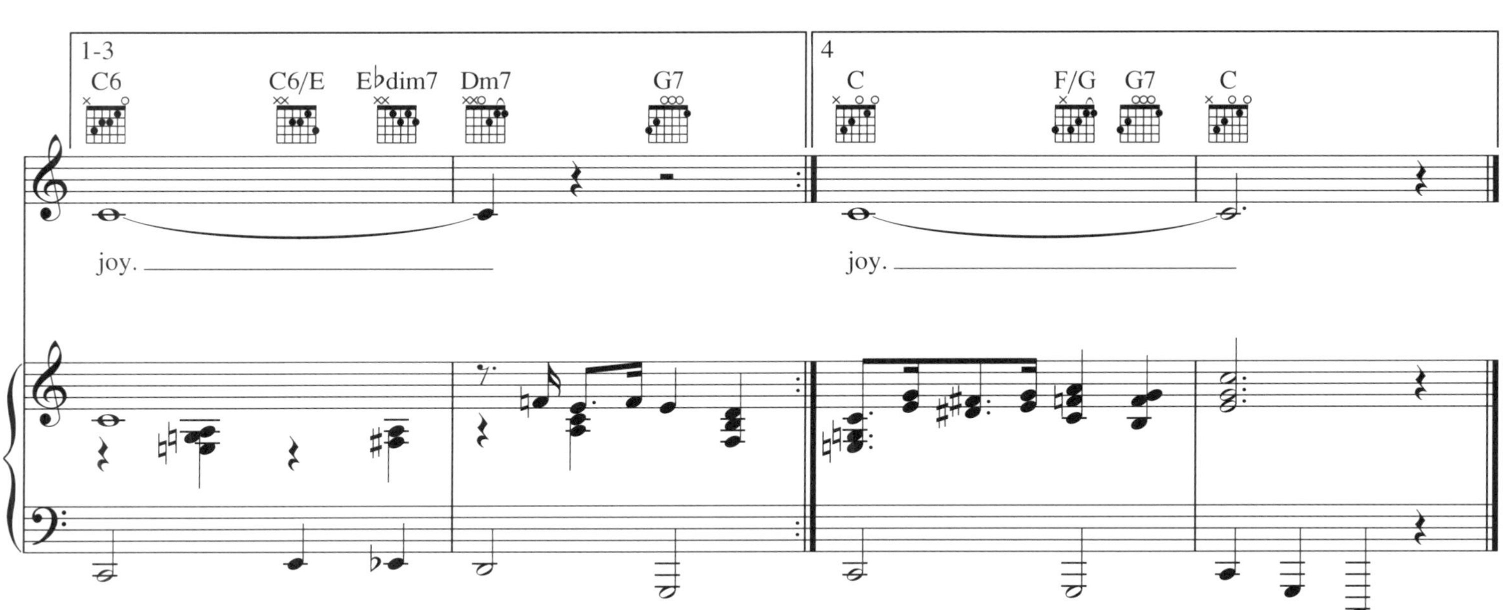
1-3
C6
C6/E
E♭dim7
Dm7
G7
4
C
F/G
G7
C
joy.
joy.

MY FAVORITE THINGS

from THE SOUND OF MUSIC

Lyrics by OSCAR HAMMERSTEIN II
Music by RICHARD RODGERS

Em
Cream - col - ored po - nies and crisp ap - ple
mf
mp
Cmaj7
stru - dels, Door - bells and sleigh - bells and schnitz - el with noo - dles,
Am7
D7
G/B
C/E
G/D
Wild geese that fly with the moon on their wings, These are a
C
F♯m7♭5
4fr
B7
E
few of my fa - vor - ite things.
f

A
Girls in white dress - es with blue sat - in sash - es, Snow - flakes that
mf
Am7
D7
stay on my nose and eye - lash - es, Sil - ver white win - ters that
G/B
C/E
G/D
C
F♯m7♭5
4fr
B7♭9
melt in - to springs, These are a few of my fa - vor - ite things.
Em
F♯m7♭5
4fr
B7
When the dog bites, When the bee stings,
mf

Em
C
When I'm feel - ing sad, I
A7/C♯
A7
sim - ply re - mem - ber my fa - vor - ite things and
G/D
C/D
G/D
C/D
G
D7♭9
4fr
D7
G
then I don't feel so bad.
cresc.
f
C
G/D
D7
G
sf

MY FUNNY VALENTINE

from BABES IN ARMS

Words by LORENZ HART
Music by RICHARD RODGERS

G
Cm
3fr
Fm
made, thy va - cant brow and thy tous - led hair con -
Eb
3fr
Cm
3fr
ceal thy good in - tent. Thou no - ble, up - right,
Bb7
Cm
3fr
G7
G7#5
truth - ful, sin - cere and slight - ly dop - ey gent, you're
Cm
3fr
Cm(maj7)
8fr
Cm7
3fr
my
My
fun - ny val - en - tine, sweet com - ic
p

Cm6
3fr
Fm/C
Fm
val - en - tine, You make me smile with my
Dm7♭5
G7
Fm/A♭
G7
heart.
Cm
3fr
Cm(maj7)
8fr
Cm7
3fr
Your looks are laugh - a - ble, un - pho - to -
F7/C
3fr
Fm/C
Fm7
graph - a - ble, yet you're my fav - 'rite work of

A♭m/C♭
A♭m/F
B♭7
B♭/A♭
E♭/G
B♭7
art. Is your fig - ure less than
E♭/G
B♭7
E♭6/G
B♭7
E♭/G
B♭7
Greek; is your mouth a lit - tle weak, when you
E♭maj7/G
G7
Cm
A♭maj7
A♭6
o - pen it to speak, are you smart?
A♭7
G7
Cm
Cm(maj7)
But don't change a hair for me,
mf
p

Cm7
F7/C
Fm7/C
not if you care for me, stay, lit - tle
poco a poco cresc.
D7♭5/A♭
G7
Cm
E♭7
val - en - tine, stay!
molto espress.
A♭
A♭maj7/G
Fm7
B♭7
1
E♭
Each day is Val - en - tine's Day.
mf
A♭7
G7
2
E♭
E♭6
Day.
8vb

NO MOON

from TITANIC

Music and Lyrics by
MAURY YESTON

Em7
Fmaj9
Fmaj7/C
spy things by.
No wave,
Dm9sus4
Dm
Bm7♭5
E7sus4
E7
no swell, no line where sea meets sky.
G/A
Am/E
G/F
F/C
Dm7
Still - ness, dark - ness. "Can't see a
G7
C
Fmaj9
Bm7♭5
G♯°7
thing," says I. No re - flec - tion, not a

Am
F♯m7♭5
B♭
Am/E
E7
Am
A sus4 sus2
shad - ow, not a glint of light meets the eye.
A5
A sus4 sus2
A
Asus4
Em7
And we go sail - ing, sail -
C/E
Dm7
Bm7♭5/D
E
Am
ing ev - er west - ward on the sea. We go
Fmaj7
G7
C
F
Bm7♭5
sail - ing, sail - ing, ev - er

Am/E
E7
Am
B/A
E/A
Am
on go we...
mp
A7
Dm/A
Am/E
E7
To Coda
A5
A sus4 sus2
p
A5
A sus4 sus2
Dm6/A
Amadd2
A - head we plow
Dm/A
Amadd2
in - to the dark - en - ing night. Can't

G9
Amadd2
see
the
bow...
How
then
to
cresc.
Fmaj7♯5
F°7
Am/E
Esus4
search
with
on
-
ly
Fmaj9
E7♭9
D.S. al Coda
star
-
light?
Coda
A5
Asus4 sus2
Am
poco rit.

OH, WHAT A BEAUTIFUL MORNIN'

from OKLAHOMA!

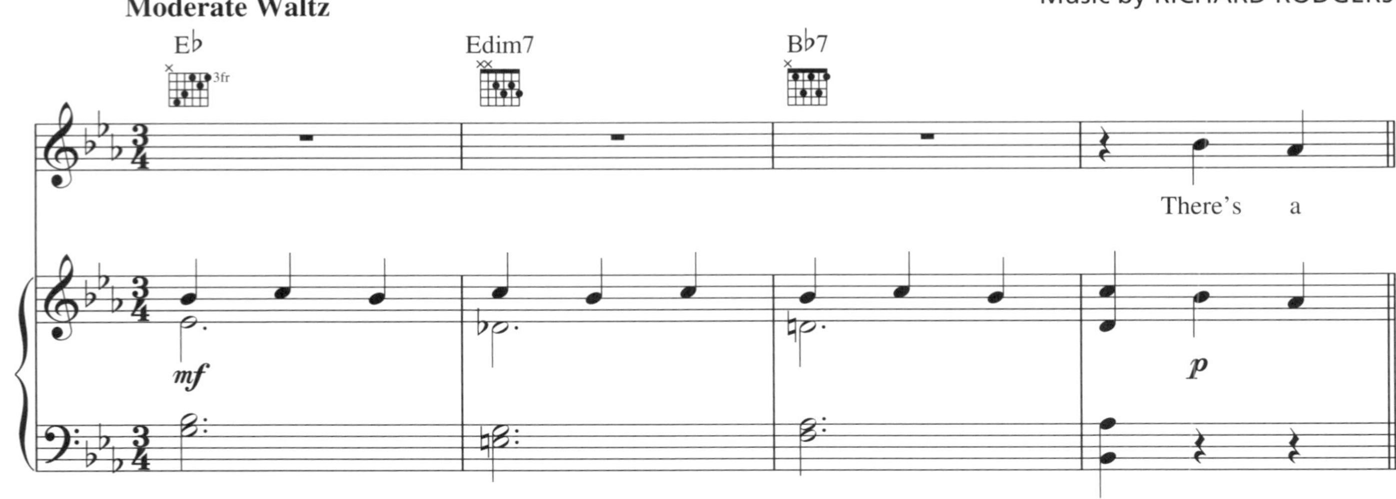

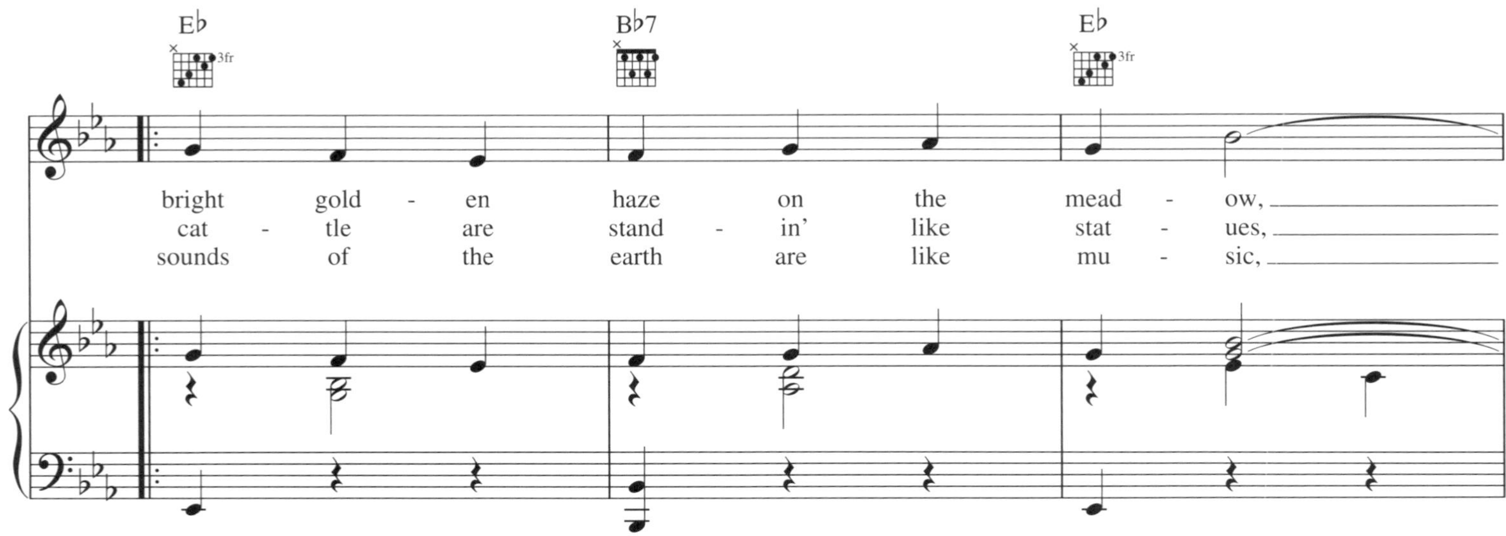

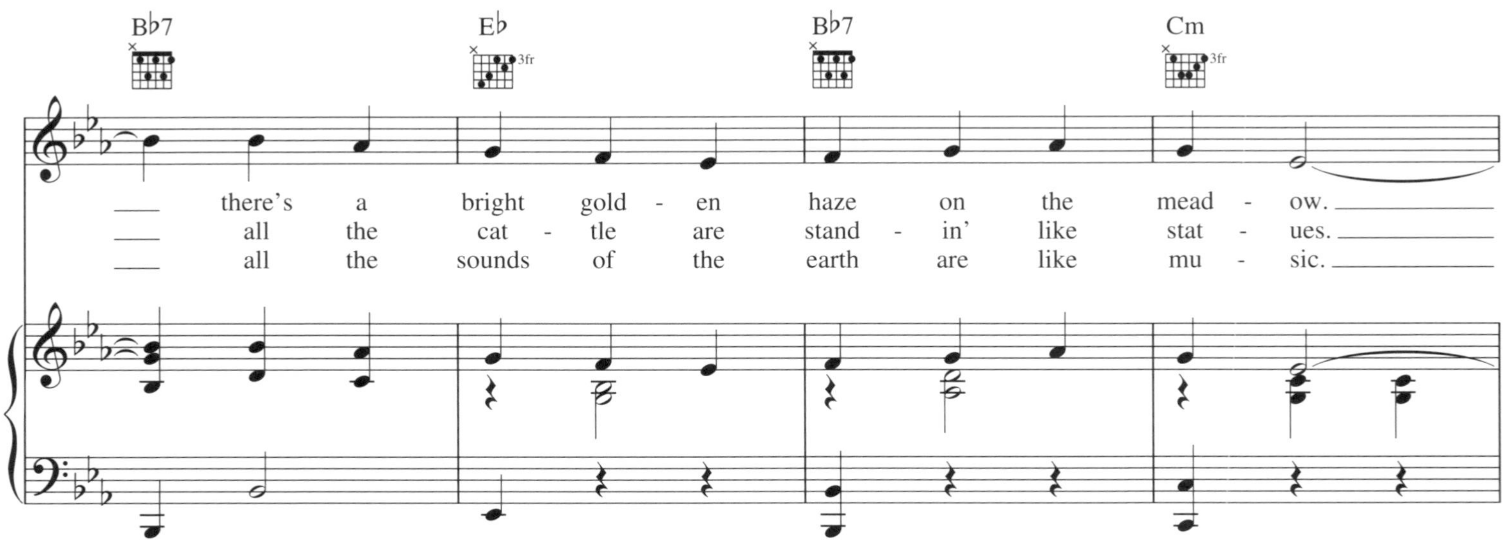

A♭m/C♭
E♭/B♭
B♭7/A♭
E♭/G
The corn is as high as an el - e - phant's
They don't turn their heads as they see me ride
The breeze is so bus - y it don't miss a
A♭
E♭
eye, an' it looks like it's climb - in' clear
by, but a lit - tle brown mav' - rick is
tree, and a ol' weep - in' wil - ler is
mf
B♭dim
B♭7
E♭
up to the sky.
wink - in' her eye.
laugh - in' at me!
Oh, what a beau - ti - ful
mp
A♭sus
A♭
E♭
morn - in'.
Oh, what a beau - ti - ful

B♭7
E♭
day.
I got a beau - ti - ful
A♭
Adim
E♭
B♭7
feel - in'.
Ev - 'ry - thing's go - in' my
1, 2
E♭
B♭7
3
E♭
Fm7/B♭
B♭7
way.
All the
All the
way.
p
riten.
E♭
B♭7
E♭
Oh, what a beau - ti - ful day!

OL' MAN RIVER

from SHOW BOAT

Lyrics by OSCAR HAMMERSTEIN II
Music by JEROME KERN

Gm
Cm6/G
Gm
Cm6
Gm
Gm7
D7
don't look down, you don't dast make de white boss frown.
Gm
Cm6/G
Gm
Cdim7/G
Gm
Gm7
Am7/G
Cdim7/G
Bend yo' knees an' bow yo' head, an' pull dat rope un -
rall.
Gm
Fm7
B♭7
E♭7
A♭
til yo're dead. Let me go 'way from de Mis - sis - sip - pi,
a tempo
C7
Fm
Ddim7
let me go 'way from de white men boss. Show me dat stream called de

E♭ D♭7 B♭7 E♭ A♭m/B♭ B♭7
3fr 4fr 3fr 4fr
riv - er Jor - dan. Dat's de ol' stream dat I long to cross.
rall.
Slower
E♭ Cm E♭ A♭ E♭ A♭
Ol' man riv - er, dat ol' man riv - er; he must know sump - in', but
legato
E♭ Cm B♭7 B♭7sus B♭7
don't say noth - in'. He jus' keeps roll - in', he keeps on roll - in' a -
E♭ A♭6 E♭ Cm
long. He don't plant 'ta - ters, he

E♭ A♭ E♭ Cm E♭/G G♭dim7
3fr 4fr 3fr 3fr 3fr 4fr
don't plant cot - ton, an' dem dat plants 'em is soon for - got - ten. But
B♭7/F Fm7/B♭ Fm7 B♭9 E♭ A♭
3fr 4fr
ol' man riv - er, he jus' keeps roll - in' a - long.
E♭ Cm/E♭ D7 Gm D7 Gm D7
3fr 3fr 3fr 3fr
You an' me, we sweat an' strain,
Gm6 D7♭9 Gm D7 Gm Cm6/G
3fr 4fr 3fr 3fr
bod - y all ach - in' an' racked wid pain. "Tote dat barge!"

Gm
Cdim7/G
Gm
Cdim7/G
Gm
A♭6
B♭7
"Lift dat bale," Git a lit - tle drunk an' you land in jail.
E♭
Cm
E♭
A♭
E♭
B♭7
Ah gits wea - ry an' sick of try - in'. Ah'm tired of liv - in' an'
Cm
F7
E♭/B♭
Cm
Fm9
B♭7
skeered of dy - in'. But ol' man riv - er, he jus' keeps roll - in' a -
rit.
1
E♭
A♭m
E♭/G
Fm7
B♭7
long.
2
E♭
Fm7
B♭9
E♭
long.

OKLAHOMA

from OKLAHOMA!

Lyrics by OSCAR HAMMERSTEIN II
Music by RICHARD RODGERS

Em7(add4)
A
Em7add4)
A
Em7(add4)
A
Dm
cat - tle, spin - ach and ter - may - ters! Flow - ers on the
prai - rie where the June bugs zoom, plen' - y of
C
air and plen' - y of room, plen' - y of
F
room to swing a rope! Plen' - y of
G7
C
Dm7

C/E
F
C/E
Dm7
C
Am
heart and plen' - y of hope.
G7
C
O -
F
C
G7
- k - la - hom - a where the wind comes
Gdim
G7sus
G7
C9
sweep - in' down the plain, and the wav - in'

F6
Dm7♭5
C
Csus
wheat can sure smell sweet when the wind comes
A7
D7
G7
C
right be - hind the rain.
O -
F
C
G7
- k - la - hom - a ev - 'ry night my
Gdim
G7sus
G7
C9
hon - ey lamb and I, sit a - lone and

F6
Dm7♭5
C
talk and watch a hawk mak - in' laz - y
G7
C
F
cir - cles in the sky.
We know we be -
C
G
long to the land
and the land we be -
D7
G9
Em
G7
C
long to is grand!
And when we say
fp

F
C
D7
(Yell)
yeeow! A - yip - i - o - ee - ay!
G
D7
C
We're on - ly say - in' you're do - in'
E7
Am
Am/G
D7/F♯
D7
C
G7
fine, Ok - la - hom - a! Ok - la - hom - a
1
C
Adim7/G
G7
2
C
O. K. K.

ON MY OWN

from LES MISÉRABLES

Music by CLAUDE-MICHEL SCHÖNBERG
Lyrics by ALAIN BOUBLIL, JOHN CAIRD,
TREVOR NUNN, JEAN-MARC NATEL
and HERBERT KRETZMER

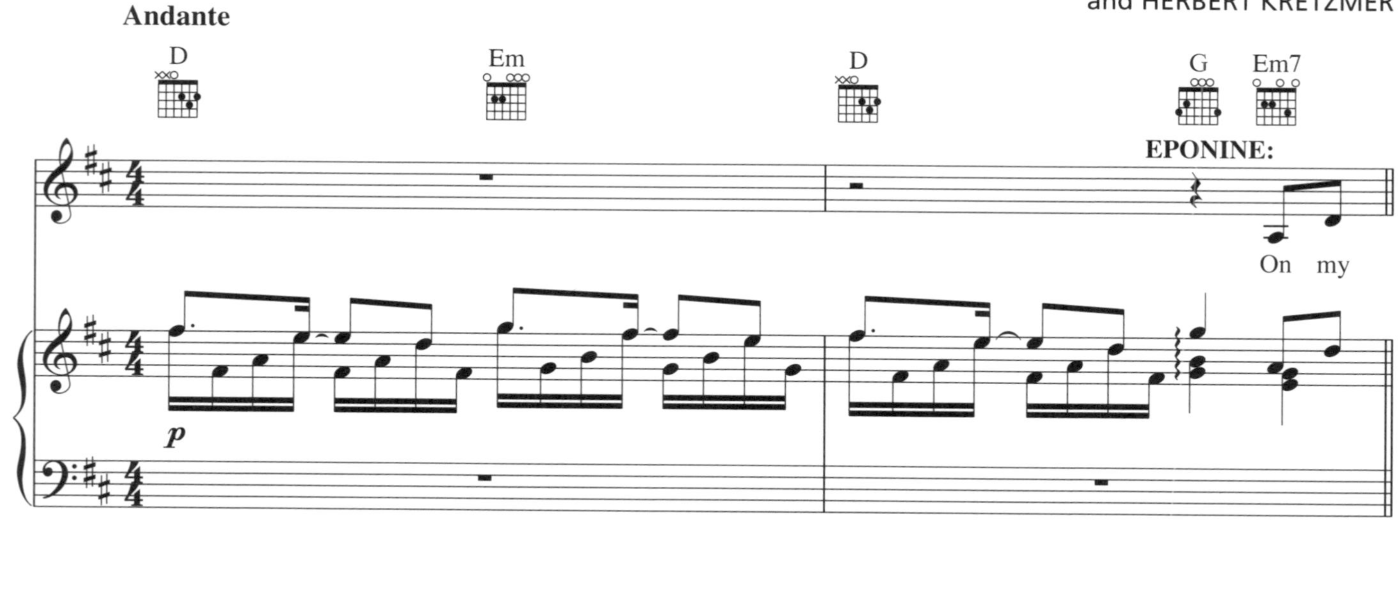

G
F♯7
Bm
him I feel his arms a - round me. And
dark - ness the trees are full of star - light. And
Em
Em/D
1 A
when I lose my way I close my eyes and he has found me. In the
all I see is him and me for - ev - er and for -
2 A
B♭
E♭m/B♭
6fr
ev - er. And I know it's on - ly in my
mf
più mosso
B♭
B♭/A
Gm
3fr
Gm/F
mind that I'm talk - ing to my - self and not to

E♭ Em

him. And al - though I know that he is

B B7 Am7 C7

blind, Still I say there's a way for us. I

F Gm/F F F/E

love him, ___ but when the night is o - ver, ___ he is

Dm G7 C C/B

gone, the riv - er's just a riv - er. With -

B♭
A
Dm
out him the world a-round me chang-es. The
Gm
Gm/F
C
trees are bare and ev-'ry-where the streets are full of stran-gers. I
F
Gm/F
F
F/E
love him but ev-'ry day I'm learn-ing all my
Dm
G7
C
C/B
life I've on-ly been pre-tend-ing. With-

B♭
A
Dm
out me his world will go on turn - ing. The
Gm
3fr
C
world is full of hap - pi - ness that I have nev - er known. I
p
F(add9)
F7/E♭
love him, I love him, I
Dm7
B♭m/D♭
F
love him, but on - ly on my own.
rall.

ONE NIGHT IN BANGKOK

from CHESS

Words and Music by BENNY ANDERSSON, TIM RICE and BJORN ULVAEUS

*Piano top line also vocal top line.

to Coda
Dm
B♭
F
C/E
Dm
You'll find a god in ev-ery gold-en cloister and if you're
Gm
luck-y then the god's a she.
I can feel an an-gel slid-ing up to me.
Dm
The American
One town's ve-ry like an-oth-er when your head's down ov-er your pie-ces, broth-er.
Choir
It's a
drag, it's a bore, it's real-ly such a pi-ty to be look-ing at the board, not look-ing at the ci-ty.

The American
Gm7
Whad-dy-a mean? You've seen one crowd-ed, pol-lu-ted, stink-ing town –
Dm
Choir
Tea, girls – warm and sweet – some are set up in the Som-er-set Maugham suite.
(warm, sweet)
The American
Get Thai'd! You're talk-ing to a tour-ist whose ev-ery move's a-mong the pur-est.
Gm7
I get my kicks a-bove the waist-line, sun-shine!
Gm7
C♯o

Choir
Dm
B♭
F
C/E
Dm
One night in Bang-kok makes a hard man hum-ble, not much between
Gm
Dm
B♭
de-spair and ec-sta-sy. One night in Bang-kok and the
F
C/E
Dm
Gm
tough guys tum-ble, can't be too care-ful with your com-pa-ny.
Gm
Dm
I can feel the dev-il walk-ing next to me.

Am
Flute solo on scale
1.
2. Am
D.S. al Coda
Coda
Dm
clois - ter, a lit - tle
Gm
flesh, a lit - tle his - to - ry.
I can feel an an -
Gm
Dm
B♭
F
C/E
- gel slid - ing up to me.
One night in Bang - kok makes a hard man

Dm
Gm
hum - ble, not much be - tween de - spair and ec - sta - sy.
Dm
B♭
F
C/E
Dm
One night in Bang - kok and the tough guys tum - ble, can't be too care -
Gm
- ful with your com - pa - ny.
I can feel the dev -
(Dm)
(Vibrato on 8:ths)
Dm9
- il walk - ing next to me.

ONCE IN LOVE WITH AMY

from WHERE'S CHARLEY?

By FRANK LOESSER

C G Am7 G B7 E7 Am7 D9
po- et-ry and flow-ers, Moon a mil- lion hours a- way. You might be quite the fick- le heart- ed
Gmaj7 C7 Gmaj7 C9 Gmaj7 E9 Am7 D9 Gmaj7
ro- ver, So care- free and bold Who loves a girl and la- ter thinks it o- ver And
D A7 D7 G G#dim Am7 D7 G G#dim
just quits cold, But Once In Love With A-my, Al-ways in love with
Am7 D7 G C G Am7 G
A-my. Ev-er and ev-er sweet- ly you'll ro-mance 'er. Trou- ble is, the an-swer will
B7 E7 Am7 A9 D7 G
be That A- my'd rath- er stay in love with me.

PEOPLE WILL SAY WE'RE IN LOVE

from OKLAHOMA!

Lyrics by OSCAR HAMMERSTEIN II
Music by RICHARD RODGERS

Em
A7
Dm
D7
prove what they say is quite un - true.
carved our i - ni - tials on the tree!
G
Gm
3fr
D
D/C
Here is the gist, a prac - ti - cal list of "don'ts" for
Jist keep a slice of all the ad - vice you give so
G/B
G7
C
you. Don't throw bou - quets at me.
free. Don't praise my charm too much.
mf
G7
Don't please my folks too much.
Don't look so vain with me.

C
Don't laugh at my
Don't stand in the
D9
4fr
Dm7
G7♭9
jokes too much. Peo - ple will say we're in
rain with me. Peo - ple will say we're in
C
C♯dim7
G7
C
love! Don't sigh and
love! Don't take my
gaze at me. Your sighs are
arm too much. Don't keep your

G7
C
so like mine.
hand in mine.
Your eyes must-n't
Your hand feels so
D9
4fr
Dm7
glow like mine.
grand in mine.
Peo - ple will
Peo - ple will
G7
C
Cm7
3fr
F7
say we're in love!
say we're in love!
Don't start
Don't dance
F7♭9
B♭+
B♭
Bm7♭5
E7
col - lect - ing things.
all night with me.
Give me my
Till the stars

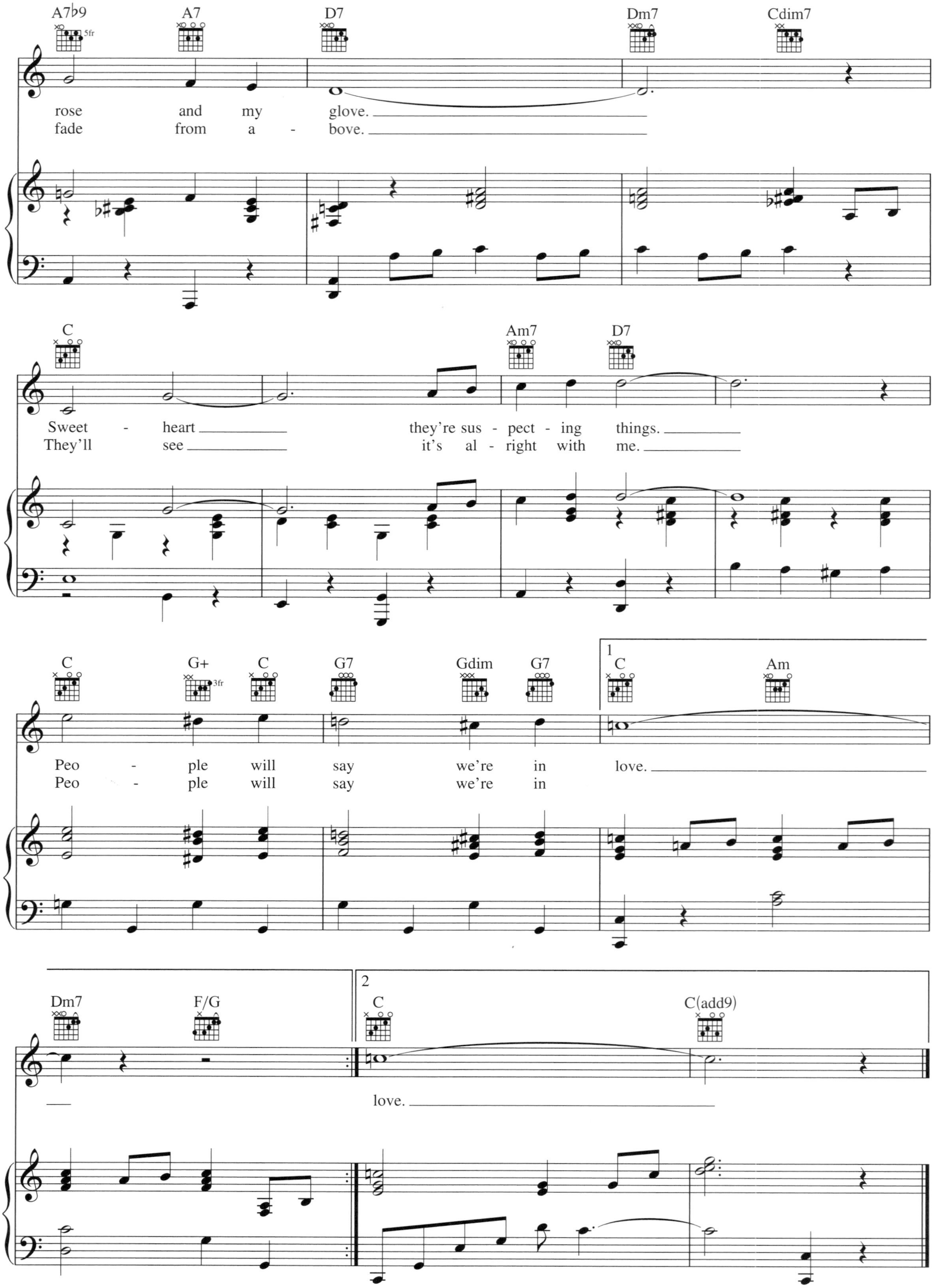
A7♭9 A7 D7 Dm7 Cdim7
5fr
rose and my glove.
fade from a - bove.
C Am7 D7
Sweet - heart they're sus - pect - ing things.
They'll see it's al - right with me.
C G+ C G7 Gdim G7
3fr
1
C Am
Peo - ple will say we're in love.
Peo - ple will say we're in
Dm7 F/G
2
C C(add9)
love.

PUT ON A HAPPY FACE

from BYE BYE BIRDIE

Lyric by LEE ADAMS
Music by CHARLES STROUSE

G7
C7
F7
B♭7
E♭maj7
3fr
E♭7
E♭6
mask of trag - e - dy, it's not your style;
A♭maj7
D7
G7
C7
F7
Fm7
You'll look so good that you'll be glad ya' de - cid - ed to smile!
B♭9
E♭
3fr
E♭6
Gm7
C7
Pick out a pleas - ant out - look,
Fm7
B♭9
Fm7
B♭9
E♭
3fr
E♭6
stick out that no - ble chin; Wipe off that "full of

Gm7
C7
Fm7
B♭9
B♭m7
E♭7
doubt" look,
slap on a hap - py grin! And
A♭maj7
B♭9
E♭
3fr
Fm7
B♭7
spread sun - shine all o - ver the
G7♯5
G7
C9
F9
Fm7
B♭9
place, just put on a hap - py
1
E♭
E♭6
Fm7
B♭7
face!
2
E♭
E♭6
Fm7
E♭
face!

PROMISES, PROMISES

from PROMISES, PROMISES

Lyric by HAL DAVID
Music by BURT BACHARACH

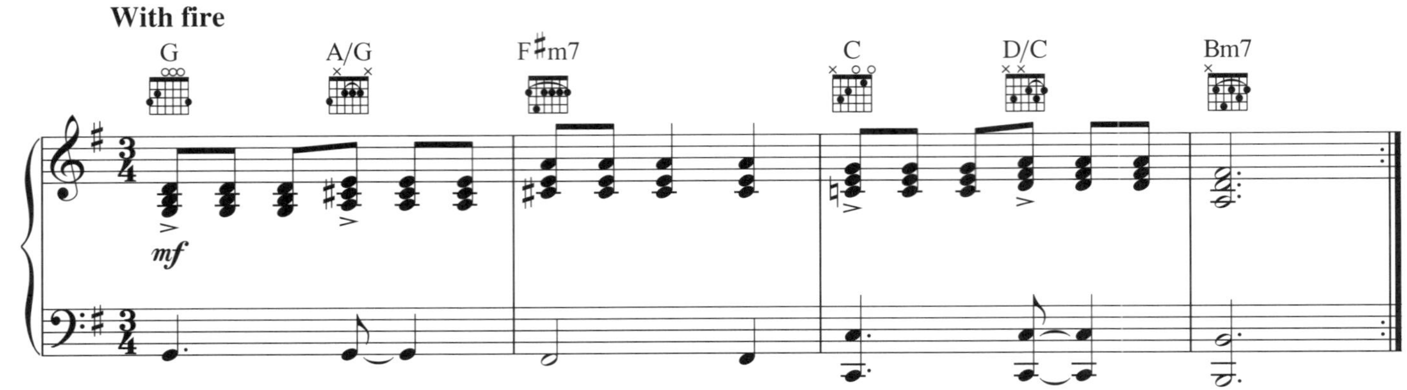

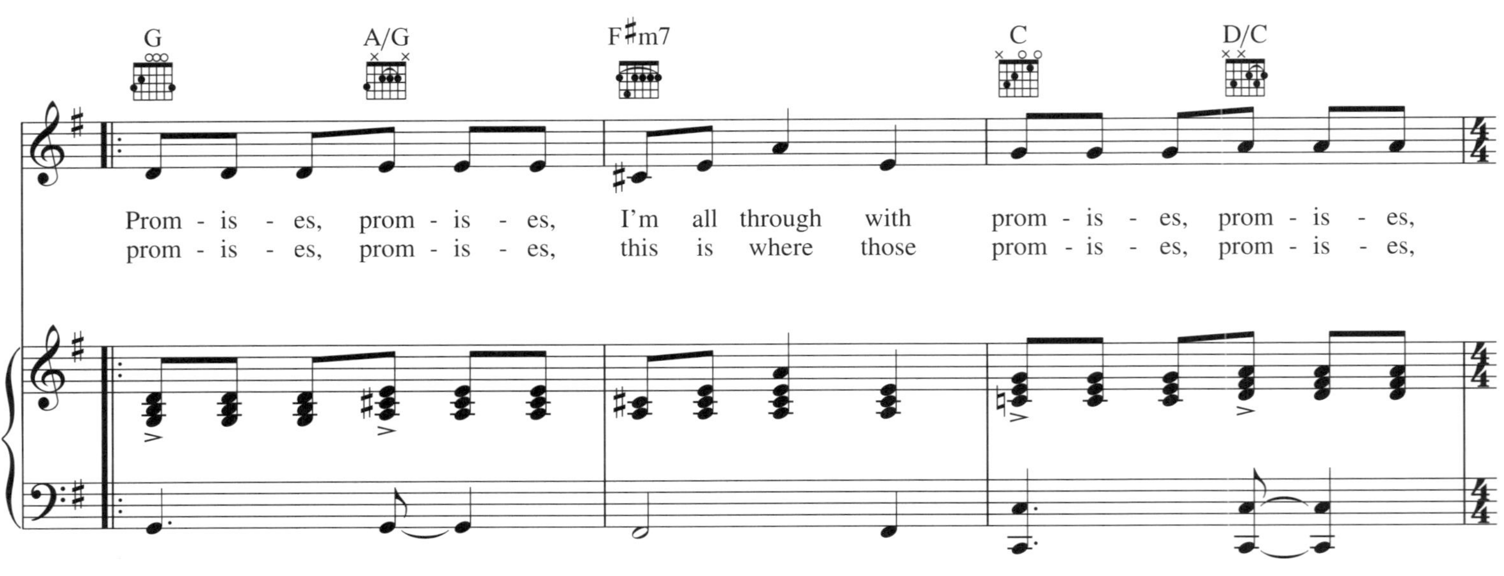

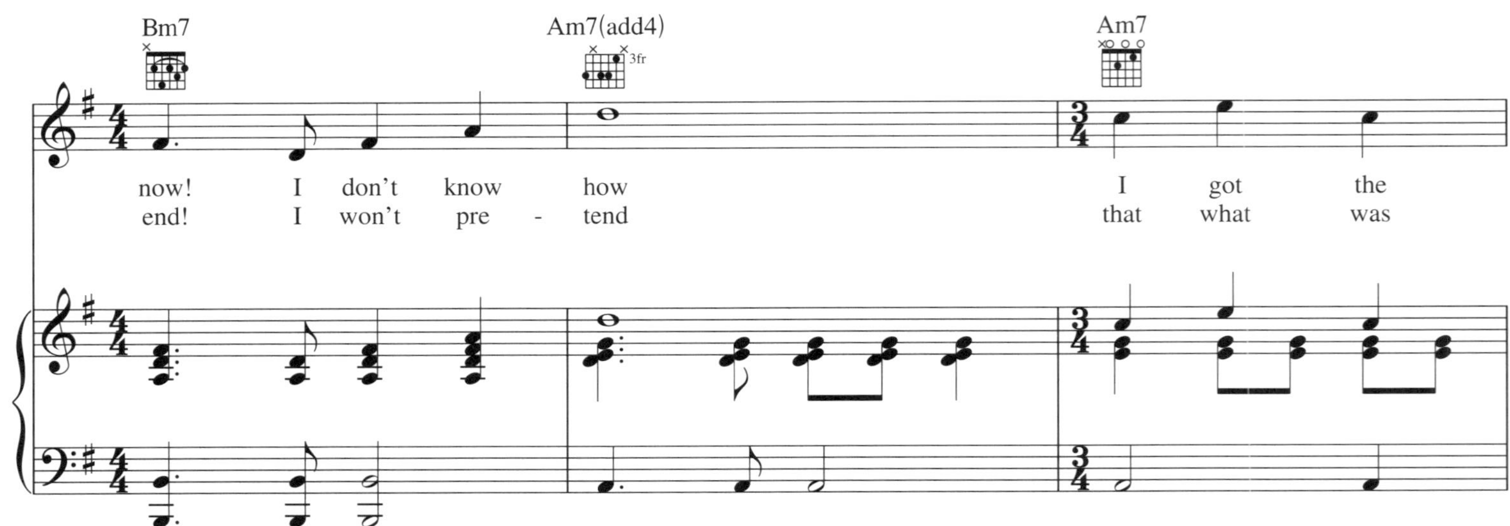

C/D
Gmaj7
nerve to walk out. If I
wrong can be right. Ev - 'ry
Cmaj7
Fmaj7(add6)
Cmaj7
shout, re - mem - ber I feel
night I'll sleep now. No more
Fmaj7(add6)
B♭maj7
free. Now I can look at my -
lies. Things that I prom - ised my -
B♭9♯11
Am7(add4)
3fr
self and be proud.
self fell a - part,

D9
Gmaj7
G6
I'm laugh - ing out loud!
but I found my heart.
Gmaj7
G6
Gmaj7
Oh,
G
A/G
C
D/C
Bm7
Prom-is - es, their kind of prom-is - es can just de-stroy your life. Oh,
prom-is - es, those kind of prom-is - es take all the joy from life! Oh,

G
A/G
C
D/C
prom - is - es, prom - is - es, my kind of prom - is - es
N.C.
Gmaj7
G6/9
can lead to joy and hope and
F6/G
F6/D
F6/G
Bmaj7
B6
love, yes, love.
rit.
a tempo
Bmaj7
B6
Bmaj7
Gmaj9
Gmaj7
Gmaj9
Gmaj7
G

RIVER IN THE RAIN

from BIG RIVER

Words and Music by
ROGER MILLER

D
wind - in' some - place just tryin' to find the sun.
A7/E
Wheth-er the sun - shine, wheth-er the rain,
A7
G
D
G
riv-er, I love you just the same. But some-times in a time of trou-ble
D/F#
Em7
D
A7
when you're out of hand and your mud - dy bub - bles roll a-cross my

D
Em7
D/F♯
G
floor
car-ryin' way the things I treas-ure;
D/F♯
Em7
D
hell, there ain't no way to meas - ure why I love you more than I
A7
did the day be - fore.
Riv - er in the rain,
G
some-times at night you look like a

D
long white train
wind-in' your way a-way some-where.
wind-in' your way a-way from me.
To Coda
A7/E
A7
G
D
D.S. al Coda
River, I love you. Don't you care? But some-times in a
CODA
A7
G
D
A7/D
Gmaj7/D
A/D
River, I've nev-er seen the sea.
8va
p
D
A7/D
Gmaj7
A5
D5
8va

SEASONS OF LOVE

from RENT

Words and Music by
JONATHAN LARSON

B♭sus2 Am7 Gm7 C7sus F C Dm Am B♭sus2 Am7
day-lights, in sun-sets, in mid-nights, in cups of cof-fee, in inch-es, in miles, in
Gm7 C7sus Dm Am B♭sus2 Am7 Gm7 C7sus F C Dm Am
laugh-ter, in strife, in five hun-dred twen-ty-five thou-sand six hun-dred min-utes. How
B♭sus2 Am7 Gm7 C7sus Dm Am E♭/B♭ B♭
do you meas-ure a year in the life? How a-bout love?
6fr
B♭/F F E♭/B♭ B♭ Dm/C C
How a-bout love? How a-bout

E♭/B♭
B♭
Gm/F
F
E♭(add2)
love? Meas-ure in love.
C9sus
B♭sus2
Am7
Gm7
C7sus
F
C
Dm
Am
Sea - sons of love, sea-sons of
love.
Five hun-dred twen-ty-five thou-sand
six hun-dred min - utes,
five hun-dred twen-ty-five thou-sand jour-neys to plan.

B♭sus2
Am7
Gm7
C7sus
F
C
Dm
Am
Five hun-dred twen-ty-five thou-sand six hun-dred min - utes. How do you meas-ure the life of a
wom-an or a man? In truth that she learned or in times that he cried, in
bridg - es he burned or the way that she died. It's time now to sing out, though the
sto-ry nev - er ends. Let's cel - e-brate, re-mem - ber a year in the life of friends. Re-mem-ber the

Eb/Bb
Bb
Bb/F
F
Eb/Bb
Bb
love, re-mem-ber the love,
Dm/C
C
Eb/Bb
Bb
Gm/F
F
re-mem-ber the love, meas-ure in
Eb(add2)
C9sus
Bbsus2
Am7
love. Sea-sons of love,
8va
Gm7
C7sus
F
C
Dm
Am
Bbsus2
Am7
Gm7
C7sus
Dm
sea-sons of love.

SMOKE GETS IN YOUR EYES

from ROBERTA

Words by OTTO HARBACH
Music by JEROME KERN

Moderately

E♭ B♭7 E♭ E♭m

mp

With pedal

B♭ B♭+ E♭ B♭7sus B♭7

They asked me how I knew my true love was

E♭/G E♭+/G A♭ Adim7 E♭/B♭

true. I, of course, re - plied, some-thing here in -

Fm7(add4) B♭7 E♭ B♭7/E♭

side can - not be de - nied.

E♭
B♭7sus
B♭7
E♭/G
E♭+/G
They said some - day you'll find all who love are blind.
A♭
Adim7
E♭/B♭
Fm7(add4)
B♭7
When your heart's on fire, you must re - al - ize smoke gets in your
E♭
B
eyes.
So I chaffed them and I
R.H.
F♯7/C♯
Cdim7
F♯7/C♯
F♯7
gay - ly laughed to think they could doubt my love.

B
A♭m7
B♭7
E♭
Yet to - day my love has flown a - way; I am with - out my
B♭7/E♭
E♭
B♭7sus
B♭7
love. Now laugh - ing friends de - ride tears I can - not
E♭/G
E♭+/G
A♭
Adim7
E♭/B♭
hide, so I smile and say, "When a love - ly flame
B♭7sus
B♭7
E♭
dies, smoke gets in your eyes."
R.H.

SEVENTY SIX TROMBONES

from Meredith Willson's THE MUSIC MAN

By MEREDITH WILLSON

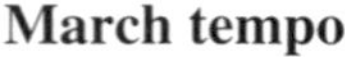

C
ten cor - nets close at hand. They were fol-lowed by
C7/B♭
5fr
F/A
D7
rows and rows of the fin - est vir - tu - o - sos, the
G
D7
G/B
D7/A
G7
cream of ev - 'ry fa - mous band. Sev - en - ty
C
E♭dim7
G7/D
C♯dim7
G7
six trom - bones caught the morn - ing sun, with a hun - dred and

C
ten cor - nets right be - hind.
There were more than a
C7/B♭
5fr
F/A
D7
thou - sand reeds spring - ing up like weeds, there were
G7
C
horns of ev - 'ry shape and kind.
There were
F
B♭/F
F
F♯dim
9fr
C7/G
C7
cop - per bot - tom tym - pa - ni in horse pla - toons,

E/C
F
C7
thun - der - ing, thun - der - ing, all a - long the way.
8vb
F
B♭/F
F
C
Dou - ble bell eu - pho - ni - ums and big bas - soons,
G7
C
G7
C7
each bas - soon hav - ing his big fat say. There were
F
B♭/F
F
F♯dim
9fr
C7/G
C7
fif - ty mount - ed can - non in the bat - ter - y,

E/C
F
C7
thun - der - ing, thun - der - ing, loud - er than be - fore.
8vb
F
B♭/F
F7/E♭
B♭/D
B♭
E7/B
E7
Clar - i - nets of ev - 'ry size and trum - pet - ers who'd im - pro - vise a
F
C7
F
full oc - tave high - er than the score.
D7
G7
Sev - en - ty

C
E♭dim7
G7/D
C♯dim7
G7
six trom - bones led the big pa - rade, when the or - der to
C
march rang out loud and clear. Start - ing off with a
C7/B♭
5fr
F/A
D7
big bang bong on a Chi - nese gong, by a
G
D7
G/B
D7/A
G7
big bang bong - er at the rear. Sev - en - ty

C
E♭dim7
G7/D
C♯dim7
G7
six trom - bones hit the coun - ter - point, while a hun - dred and
ten cor - nets played the air. Then I mod - est - ly
C7/B♭
5fr
F/A
D7
took my place as the one and on - ly bass, and I
G
G7
E♭7
oom - pahed up and down the square. Buh buh buh

A♭
E♭7
buh buh buh buh buh buh buh buh, buh buh buh buh buh
A♭
buh buh buh buh buh buh. Buh buh buh buh buh
D♭
buh buh buh buh buh buh buh buh buh buh
E♭7
B♭7
E♭7
G7
buh buh buh buh buh buh buh. Sev - en - ty

C Ebdim7 G7/D C#dim7 G7

six trom - bones hit the coun - ter - point, __ while a hun - dred and ten cor - nets played the

C C7/Bb

air. __ Then I mod - est - ly took my place as the

F/A D7 C G

one and on - ly bass, and I oom - pahed, oom - pahed,

C
G
G7
oom - pah - pahed, oom - pahed up and down the
1
C
E♭dim7
G7/D
G7
2
C
square. Sev - en - ty square.
B♭/C
C
B♭/C
C

SHALL WE DANCE?

from THE KING AND I

Lyrics by OSCAR HAMMERSTEIN II
Music by RICHARD RODGERS

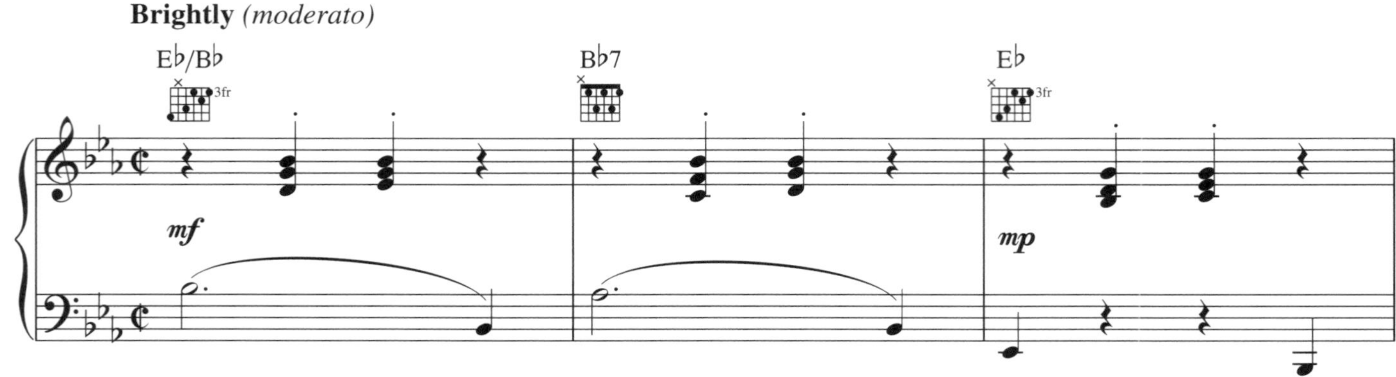

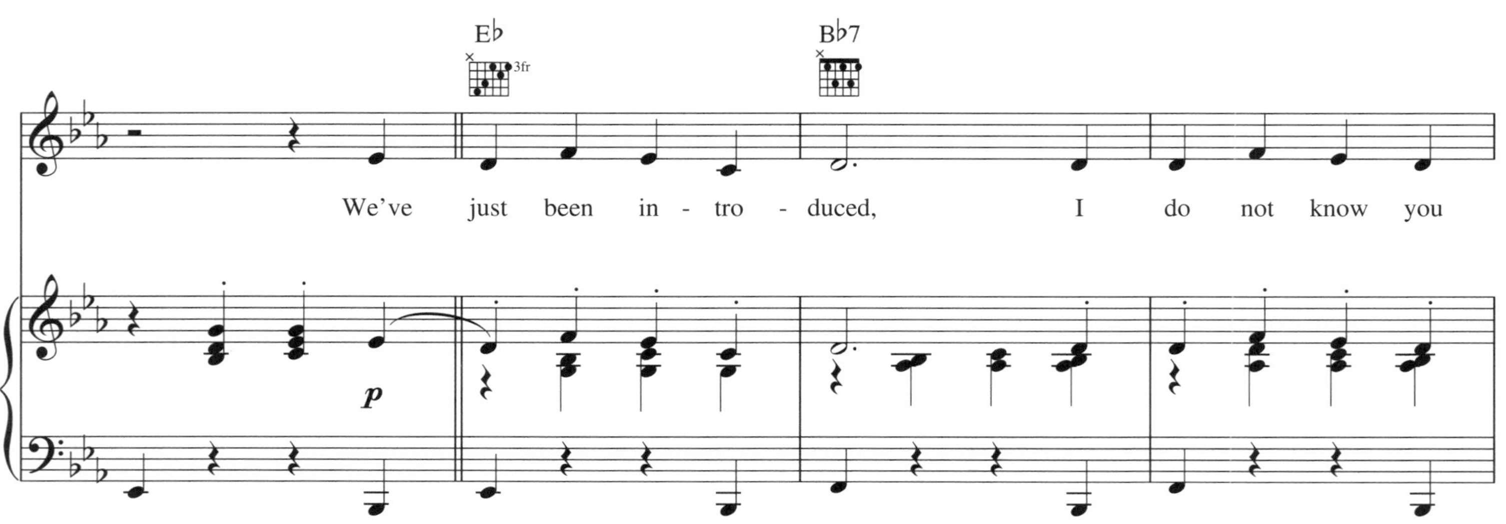

B♭7
G7
Cm
3fr
man - y men and girls Are in each oth - er's arms, It
B♭
Fdim7
F7
B♭7
B♭7♯5
made me think we might be sim - i - lar - ly oc - cu - pied. Shall we
Refrain (gaily)
E♭6
B♭7
B♭7♯5
E♭
3fr
dance? On a bright cloud of
mp
E♭6
B♭7
mu - sic shall we fly? Shall we dance?

Shall we then say "good - night" and mean "good -
E♭
bye?" Or, per - chance
E♭maj7
when the
E♭6
last lit - tle
E♭
star has left the
A♭6
sky. Shall we
B♭7
still be to - geth - er with our
E♭
arms a - round each
mf
3fr

B♭9
E♭7
oth - er, And shall you be my new ro - mance?
A♭
4fr
On the clear un - der - stand - ing that this
E♭
3fr
C7♯5
C7
Fm7
B♭7
kind of thing can hap - pen, Shall we dance? Shall we dance? Shall we
1
E♭
3fr
B♭7
B♭7♯5
2
E♭
3fr
dance? Shall we dance?
mf
mp
sf

SOME ENCHANTED EVENING

from SOUTH PACIFIC

Lyrics by OSCAR HAMMERSTEIN II
Music by RICHARD RODGERS

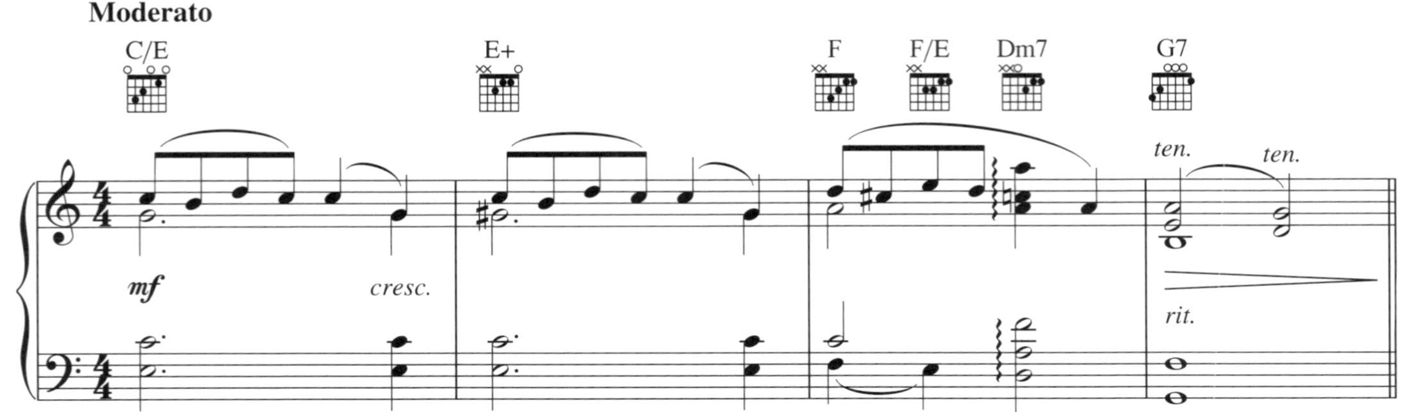

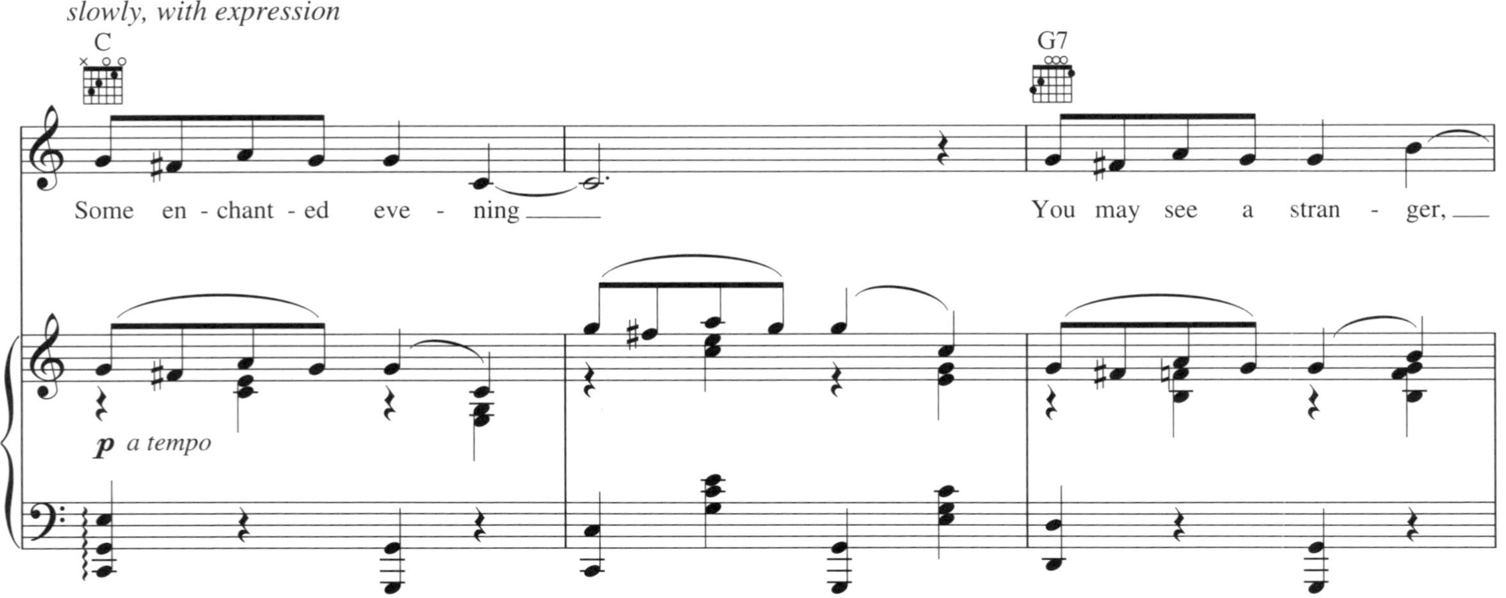

Fmaj7
F6
C6/E
Dm7
G7
Dm
E7
crowd - ed room
And some - how you
know,
You know e - ven
mf
Am
C7/G
F
C/E
Dm7
G7
then
That some - where you'll
see her
a - gain and a -
Cmaj7
C7
C+
Cdim7/G
C
gain.
Some en - chant - ed
eve - ning
p
G7
Some - one may be
laugh - ing,

C
E+
Fmaj7
F6
You may hear her laugh - ing A - cross a crowd - ed room
C6/E
Dm7
G7
Dm
E7
Am
C7/G
And night af - ter night, As strange as it seems,
F
C/E
Dm7
G7
C
The sound of her laugh - ter will sing in your dreams.
mf
G7sus
G7
Cmaj9
C
Dm7
G7
C6
C
Who can ex - plain it? Who can tell you why?
pp
tenderly and legato

G7sus
G7
Cmaj9
C
Am7
D7
G
Cm6
Fools give you reas - ons, Wise men nev - er try.
cresc. molto
Edim7
Dm7/G
Cdim7/G
C
Some en - chant - ed eve - ning
mp
Dm7
G7
C
When you find your true love,
When you feel her call you
E+
Fmaj7
F6
C6/E
A - cross a crowd - ed room,
Then fly to her
mf

Dm7
G7
Dm7
E7
Am
C7/G
F
C/E
side
And make her your own,
Or all through your
molto espr.
Dm
Dm7/G
G7
C
life you may dream all a - lone.
rit.
a tempo
dim.
G7sus
G7
Cmaj9
C
Dm7
G7
C6
C
Once you have found her, Nev - er let her go.
Once you have found her,
pp legatissimo
Dm7/G
C
Nev - er let her go!
rit.
mf

THE SOUND OF MUSIC

from THE SOUND OF MUSIC

Lyrics by OSCAR HAMMERSTEIN II
Music by RICHARD RODGERS

C7
F
Fm6
voic - es that urge me to stay.
So I pause and I wait and I
E♭
3fr
C7
F
Gm
3fr
C7
lis - ten for one more sound, For one more love - ly thing that the hills might
rit.
Refrain (moderately, with warm expression)
F
F(add9)
E/F
say. The hills are a - live with the sound of mu - sic,
più rit.
p a tempo
F6
B♭/D
With songs they have sung for a thou - sand years.
3

C7
F(add9)
E/F
The hills fill my heart with the sound of mu - sic.
F/A
B♭/D
C6
C7
F
My heart wants to sing ev - 'ry song it hears.
B♭
B♭dim7
F/A
F/C
B♭
B♭dim7
My heart wants to beat like the wings of the birds that rise from the lake to the
mp
F/A
F/C
B♭
B♭dim7
F/A
F/C
G7/D
D♭7♭5
8fr
trees. My heart wants to sigh like a chime that flies from a church on a

C F/A B♭ B♭dim7 F/A F/C
breeze, To laugh like a brook when it trips and falls o - ver
B♭ B♭dim7 F/A F/C Dm Dm6 Am
stones in its way, To sing through the night like a
Dm G7 C C7 F(add9)
lark who is learn - ing to pray. I go to the hills
mp
E/F
when my heart is lone - ly. I

F6/9
B♭/D
know I will hear what I've heard be - fore.
B♭m/D♭
F/C
Am/C
My heart will be blessed with the sound of
mf più espressivo
B♭
Gm7
Am/C
C7
mu - sic And I'll sing once
dim.
1
F
Fdim
Gm7/F
C7
2
F
more. The more.
p
mp

SOMEBODY LOVES ME

from GEORGE WHITE'S SCANDALS OF 1924

Words by B.G. DeSYLVA and BALLARD MacDONALD
Music by GEORGE GERSHWIN
French Version by EMELIA RENAUD

G Am/D D7 G6 Am7 D7sus D7 G7 G7/C Cmaj7
some - one has up - set, Heav - en's pret - ty pro - gram for we've
Cm6 D7 Em Em6 Bm Bm7 Bm6 E7
2 fr
7 fr
nev - er met. I'm clutch-ing at straws, just be - cause
Em7/A A7 D7 D7♯5 G Am7 Am/D D
I may meet her yet. Some - bod - y loves me
G C7 G C7 Am7 D7
I won - der who, I won - der who she can be. _
3

G
D7♭9
G
4 fr
Some - bod - y
Am7
Am/D
D
G
A7
loves me I wish I knew,
Bm
C♯7♭9
C♯m7/F♯
4 fr
F♯7
Bm
Bm(maj7)
2 fr
who can she be wor - ries me.
Bm7
2 fr
E7
Am
Dm6/A
Am
Dm6/A
For ev - 'ry girl who pass - es me I shout, Hey!

Am
Em7
A7
Em7
A7
may - be. You were meant to be my lov - ing
D7
D+
G
Am7
Am/D
D
ba - by. Some - bod - y loves me
G
C7
G
Em7
Am7
D7
I won - der who, may - be it's
3
1
G
D7
you.
2
G
Am/D
G
you.

SOMEONE LIKE YOU

from JEKYLL & HYDE

Words by LESLIE BRICUSSE
Music by FRANK WILDHORN

B♭/F F C/F A/C♯
keep - ing life at bay. I wan - dered, lost in yes - ter -
I've nev - er seen be - fore. Your love has o - pened ev - 'ry
cresc.
Dm F/C B♭ Gm7 3fr C7sus C
day, want - ing to fly, but scared to try. Then
door. You've set me free, now I can soar. For
F Gm7 3fr
some - one like you found some - one like me, and
some - one like you found some - one like me. You
F F/A B♭ Gm7♭5 5fr
sud - den - ly nothing - ing is the same. My
touched my heart. Noth - ing is the same. There's a
dim.

F Dm7 Gm7 F Dm7 Gm7
3fr
heart's tak - en wing, and I feel so a - live, 'cause
new way to live, a new way to love, 'cause
1
F Dm7 Gm7 D♭/G♭ F Em7 Em7/A A7
some - one like you found me.
2
F Dm7 Gm7 C7sus D♭ B/C♯ C♯7
4fr
some - one like you found me. Oh,
molto rit.
F♯ G♯m7
some - one like you found some - one like me, and
f a tempo

F♯
F♯/A♯
B
G♯m7♭5
3fr
sud - den - ly
noth - ing will ev - er be the same. My
F♯
D♯m
G♯7sus
4fr
A♯m
C♯/D♯
D♯7♭9
heart's tak - en wing, and I feel so a - live, 'cause
p
G♯m
4fr
C♯7sus
F♯
some - one like you loves me,
much slower, freely
a tempo
Bmaj7
F♯
loves me.
rit.
pp

THE SONG IS YOU

from MUSIC IN THE AIR

Lyrics by OSCAR HAMMERSTEIN II
Music by JEROME KERN

Cmaj9
G9
9fr
C
Cdim
3fr
start, then melt a - way.
I hear mu - sic when I touch your
Dm7
G7
C
C♯dim7
hand, a beau - ti - ful mel - o - dy from some en - chant - ed
G7
Cmaj7
A7♯5
land. Down deep in my heart, I hear it
Dm
G9
9fr
C
say, "Is this the day?"

E
Emaj7
A/C♯
Dm
B9/D♯
6fr
I a - lone have heard this lone - ly strain,
Emaj7
D♯7
I a - lone have heard this glad re - frain.
G♯m
4fr
C♯9
3
Must it be for - ev - er in - side of me? Why can't I
F♯13
B13
7fr
let it go? Why can't I let you know? Why can't I
cresc.
poco rit.

C/G
Cdim/G
G7
let you know the song my heart would sing, that beau - ti - ful
C
C9
F
Fm6
rhap - so - dy of love and youth and spring? The mu - sic is
Cmaj7/E
A7#5
Dm
G9
sweet, the words are true, the song is
C
you.

THE SONG THAT GOES LIKE THIS

from MONTY PYTHON'S SPAMALOT

Lyrics by ERIC IDLE
Music by JOHN DU PREZ and ERIC IDLE

C
F
C/E
A/C♯
LADY OF THE LAKE:
Where is it? Where? Where? A sen - ti-men-tal song that casts a mag - ic spell. They
Dm
Dm9/C
3fr
B♭
F
Dm
all will hum a - long. We'll o - ver - act like hell. Oh, this is the
Gm7
3fr
C7
F
B♭/F
DENNIS:
song that goes like this. Yes, it is!
F
B♭
LADY:
DENNIS:
LADY:
DENNIS:
Yes, it is! Yes, it is! Yes, it is!
3
Now we can go straight in -
cresc.
mf

F/A
Gm7
C7
F
F7/A
LADY:
to the mid-dle eight, a bridge that is too far for me. I'll
B♭
A7
Dm
G7
BOTH:
sing it in your face, while we both em-brace, and then we change the
C
D7
G
DENNIS:
(opt. 8va)
key!
cresc.
Now we're in-to E. That's
D/F♯
Em
Em9/D
C
LADY:
BOTH:
aw-fully high for me. But ev-'ry-one can see we should have stayed in D. For

G
Em
Am7
Dsus
this is our song that goes like this.
D
G
DENNIS:
I'm feel-ing ver-y proud.
LADY:
You're
D/F♯
Em
Em9/D
sing-ing far too loud.
DENNIS:
That's the way that this song goes.
LADY:
You're
C
G
Em
Am7
stand-ing on my toes.
BOTH:
Sing - ing our song that goes like

Dsus
D
Esus
E
LADY:
this.
I
A
E/G♯
DENNIS:
LADY:
can't be-lieve there's more.
It's far too long, I'm sure.
That's the
F♯m
F♯m7/E
D
BOTH:
trou-ble with this song,
it goes on and on and on.
For
A
F♯m
Bm7
Esus
E
DENNIS:
LADY:
this is our song that is too long.

E/F♯
DENNIS:
F♯
LADY:
B
DENNIS:
Je - sus Christ! God damn it! We'll be sing-ing this till dawn. You'll
F♯/A♯
LADY:
G♯m
G♯m9/F♯
BOTH:
wish that you weren't born. Let's stop this damn re - frain, be -
E
DENNIS:
LADY:
B
G♯m
fore we go in - sane. The song al - ways
rit. poco a poco
C♯m7
F♯
F♯7
E/B
B
BOTH:
ends like this.
molto rit.
fff
All the glass on the chandelier breaks.

STARLIGHT EXPRESS

from STARLIGHT EXPRESS

Music by ANDREW LLOYD WEBBER
Lyrics by RICHARD STILGOE

B♭sus/E♭
E♭
A♭
A♭/B♭
lis-ten and you'll find
the mid-night train is get-ting near - er.
E♭
Fm/E♭
B♭/E♭
A♭/E♭
Star-light Ex - press,
Star-light Ex - press,
are you real?
Yes or
E♭maj7
Fm/E♭
E♭/B♭
no?
Star-light Ex - press,
an-swer me "yes."
I
A♭/B♭
E♭
don't want you to go.
Take me to the plac - es

B♭sus/E♭
B♭/E♭
E♭
3fr
I have nev - er been.
Bring me home safe - ly be - fore I
B♭
E♭
3fr
wake _ up. ___
I be - lieve in you com - plete - ly ___
B♭/E♭
E♭
3fr
though you may be un - seen.
This is not the kind _ of thing _ that an -
A♭
4fr
A♭/B♭
4fr
E♭
3fr
Fm/E♭
- y - one ___ should make _________ up. ___
Star - light Ex - press, ___
f

B♭/E♭
A♭/E♭
Star - light Ex - press, are you real? Yes or
E♭
Fm/E♭
E♭/B♭
no? Star-light Ex - press, an-swer me "yes." I
mf
A♭/B♭
E♭
don't want you to go.
E
F♯m/E
B/E
A6/E

Emaj7
F♯m/E
E/B
And
mp
A/B
if you're there and if you know then
cresc.
show me which way I must go.
E
F♯m/E
B/E
A/E
Star-light Ex - press, Star-light Ex - press, are you real? Yes or
f
3

E
F♯m/E
E/B
no? Star-light Ex - press, please an - swer me "yes." I
mf
A/B
E
F♯m/E
don't want you to go. Star-light Ex - press,
mp
B/E
A/E
Emaj7
F♯m7/E
you must con - fess. Are you real? Do you care? Star-light Ex - press,
E/B
A/B
E
an - swer me "yes." I need you to be there.
mp

SUNRISE, SUNSET

from the Musical FIDDLER ON THE ROOF

Words by SHELDON HARNICK
Music by JERRY BOCK

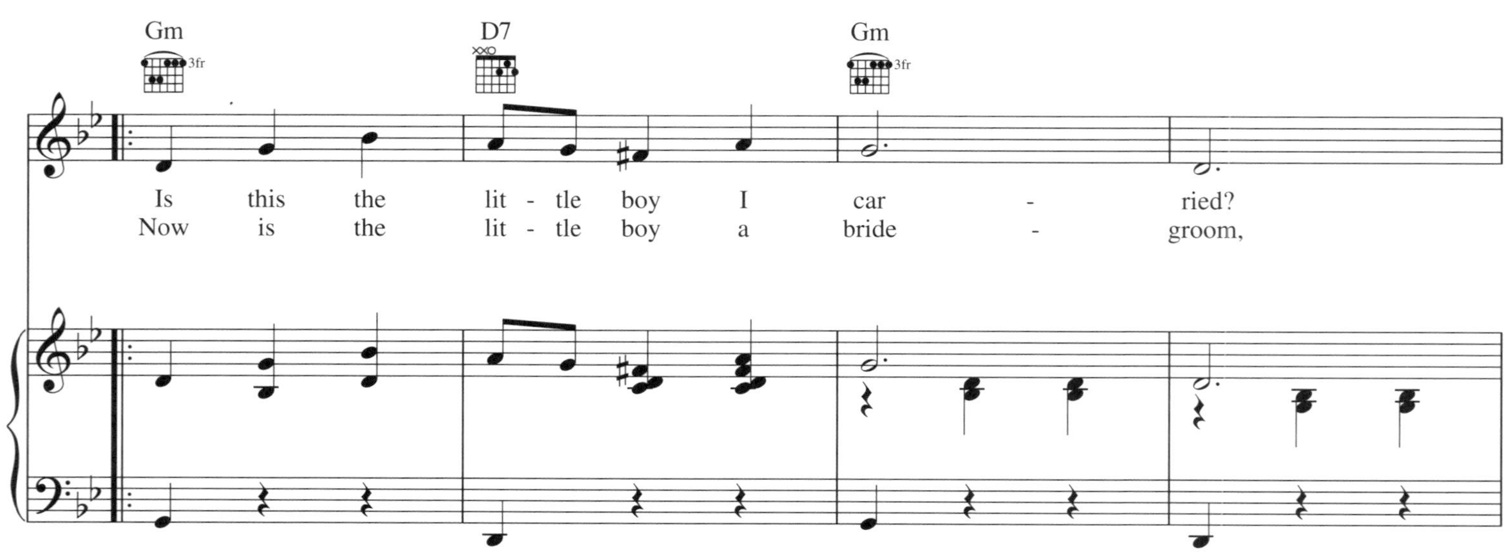

G7
Cm
A
A7
member growing old - er, when did
can - o - py I see them, side by
D7♯5
Gm
D7
Gm
they? When did she get to be a beau -
side. Place the gold ring a-round her fin -
D7
Gm
G7
ty? When did he grow to be so tall?
ger. Share the sweet wine and break the glass.
Cm
G7
Cm
A7
Was - n't it yes - ter - day when they were
Soon the full cir - cle will have come to

D
D7
D+
D7
small?
pass.
Gm
3fr
D7
Gm
3fr
D7
Gm
3fr
Sun - rise, sun - set, sun - rise, sun - set, swift - ly
flow the days.
G7
Cm
3fr
Seed - lings turn
F7
B♭maj7
B♭6
Am7
D7
o - ver-night to sun - flow'rs, blos - som - ing e - ven as we

Gm
D7
Gm
gaze.
Sun - rise,
sun - set,
sun - rise,
D7
Gm
G7
sun - set,
swift - ly
fly
the
years;
Cm
F7
B♭maj7
B♭6
Am7
one sea - son
fol - low - ing
an - oth - er,
la - den with
D7
1
Gm
2
Gm
hap - pi - ness and
tears.
tears.
rit.

TEN CENTS A DANCE

from SIMPLE SIMON

Words by LORENZ HART
Music by RICHARD RODGERS

Gm
C7
F7
Eb/Bb
Cm6
B7#5
know; one that the pal - ace fea - tures at ex - act - ly a dime a
Fm7/Bb
Bb7
Slowly, quasi rubato
Eb
F#dim7
Fm7
Bb7
Eb
F7
throw. Ten cents a dance, that's what they pay me. Gosh, how they weigh me
poco rit.
Bb7
Eb
F#dim7
Fm7
Bb7
down! Ten cents a dance, pan - sies and rough guys,
Eb7
Ab
Dm7
G7
C7b9
Fm
tough guys who tear my gown! Sev - en to mid - night, I hear drums,

C7♭9
Fm
D7
Gm
loud-ly the sax - o-phone blows,
trum-pets are tear - ing my ear-drums.
C7♭9
F7
B♭7
E♭
F♯dim7
Fm7
B♭7
Cus-tom - ers crush my toes.
Some-times I think I've found my he - ro
E♭7
A♭
Dm7
G7
C7♭9
Fm7♭5
but it's a queer ro - mance.
All that you need _ is a tick - et;
E♭/B♭
G+
A♭maj7
A7♭5
1
B♭7
E♭
B♭7♯5
2
B♭7
E♭
come on, big boy. ten cents a dance!
ten cents a dance!
8vb

Cm
Cm(maj7)
Cm7
Cm6
E♭/B♭
B♭7
Fight-ers and sail-ors and bow-leg - ged tail-ors can pay for their tick-ets and
E♭
Cm
Cm(maj7)
Cm7
Cm6
rent me! Butch-ers and bar-bers and rats from the har-bors are
E♭/B♭
B♭7♯5
E♭
Gm
E♭7/G
C/G
E♭7/G
sweet-hearts my good luck has sent me. Though I've a cho-rus of
Gm
E♭7/G
C7
Am
F7/A
D/A
F7/A
Am
F7/A
D7
el-der - ly beaux, stock-ings are por-ous with holes at the toes.
3fr
6fr

Gm
Cm7♭5
B♭/F
I'm here till clos - ing time, dance and be mer - ry, it's
F7
B♭7
E♭
F♯dim7
Fm7
B♭7
on - ly a dime. Some - times I think I've found my he - ro
E♭
Dm7
G7
C7♭9
but it's a queer ro - mance. All that you need is a
Fm7♭5
E♭/B♭
G+
A♭maj7
A7♭5
B♭6
B♭7
E♭
tick - et! Come on, big boy, ten cents a dance!

'TIL HIM
from THE PRODUCERS

Music and Lyrics by
MEL BROOKS

D7 Gm Cdim7/G G7sus G7 C7

chance, then I felt his mag - ic and my heart be - gan to dance!

Gm7/C C13 F B♭/F C7 Fmaj7

I was al - ways fright - ened, fraught with wor - ry 'til him.

mp

C7/F F(add9) C7/F Am7♭5

I was go - ing no - where in a hur - ry 'til him.

D7 B♭ Gm7♭5

He filled up my emp - ty life,

f

Am7
Am7/D
D7
G7sus
G7
B♭/C
Gm7♭5/C
filled it to the brim. There could nev - er ev - er be an - oth - er one like
poco rit.
mp a tempo
poco rit.
F
C7
F
F♯m7/B
him.
B9
E
A/E
B7/E
MAX:
No one ev - er ev - er real - ly knew me 'til
mp
E(add9)
A/E
B7
E
B7/E
B7/A
him. Ev - 'ry - one was al - ways out to screw me 'til

G♯m7♭5
C♯7♭5
8fr
C♯7
F♯m7
him.
Nev - er met a man I ev - er
B7
G♯m7
4fr
C♯7
trust - ed,
al - ways dealt with shy - sters in the past.
(
)
F♯m7
Fdim7
F♯7sus
F♯
B7sus
2fr
Now I'm well - ad - just - ed
'cause I've got a friend at
last.
poco rit.
A tempo
B9
C9
Fmaj7
B♭/F
C7/F
Al - ways play - ing sin - gles, nev - er dou - bles 'til
mp
poco rall.

F
B♭/F
C/F
3fr
F(add9)
C7/F
him. Nev - er had a pal to share my trou - bles 'til
Am7♭5
D7
Gm7
B♭m
LEO & MAX:
him. He filled up my emp - ty life,
f
Am7
Am7/D
D7
G7sus
G7
Gm7♭5
LEO:
filled it to the brim. There could nev - er ev - er be an - oth - er one
poco rit.
a tempo
poco rit.
Slowly
F
B♭/F
F(add9)
like him.

THAT FACE

from THE PRODUCERS

Music and Lyrics by
MEL BROOKS

Em7♭5/B♭
A7
Dm11
3fr
G7
C
fens - es for ev - 'ry skirt will test tes - tos - ter - one. So
E
B7
E
B7
know-ing this, I sev-ered all con - nec - tion with an - y crea-ture sport-ing silk or
più mosso
E
G
D7
G
lace. I was firm - ly head - ed in the right di - rec - tion when
D7
Slowly
Gm9
3fr
C13
2fr
sud - den - ly I stum - bled on that face. That

With a lilt, in 2
F6
Gm9
C13
F6
mf
face, that face, that dan - ger - ous face. I
F
Gm7
C7♭9
Fmaj9
F6
Gm
must - n't be un - wise. Those lips, that
F6
E/F
Gm7
C9♭5
C9
nose, those eyes could lead to my de -
F6
Dm7
G7
C7
F6
Gm7
C13
F6
mise. That face, that face, that mar - ve-lous face,

Gm7
Gm7♭5/C
F9
I nev - er should be - gin.
Those
Gm7
F6
E/F
cheeks, that neck, that chin
will
Gm9
3fr
C6♭9
F6
sure - ly do me in.
I
Cm7
3fr
F13
Cm7
3fr
F13
B♭
B♭6
must be smart and hide my heart if she's with - in a mile.
If

Dm7
G13
Dm7
G13
Gm9/A
Gm7♭5
C7
I don't duck, I'm out of luck. She'd kill me with her smile. That
rit.
colla voce
A tempo
F6
Gm7
C13
F6
face, that face, that fab - u - lous face, it's
Gm7
C7♭9
Cm9
F13
clear I must be - ware. I'm
1
B♭maj9♯11
Gm7♭5
F6/C
D+/F♯
D7♭9
Gm7
cer - tain if I fall in love, I'm lost with - out a trace, but it's worth it,

C13
F6/9
Gm7
C6/9
F6/9
Dm7
Gm9
C9
for that face.
That
2
B♭maj9♯11
Gm7♭5
F6/C
D7♯5
espressivo
cer - tain if I fall in love, I'm lost with - out a trace,
rit., freely
A tempo, in 2
Gm11
C13
F6
D♭9
but it's worth it, for that face.
rit.
F6
D♭9
F6/9

THIS NEARLY WAS MINE

from SOUTH PACIFIC

Lyrics by OSCAR HAMMERSTEIN II
Music by RICHARD RODGERS

E♭
Fm/B♭
E♭
This nearly was mine.
One
Fm7
F♯dim
E♭/G
B♭/D
D♭dim
girl for my dream,
One partner in
A♭/C
A♭m/C♭
E♭/B♭
Cm/A
paradise,
This promise of
A♭
A♭m
E♭
Fm/B♭
paradise
This nearly was

E♭
A♭
E♭7
A♭
mine.
Close to my heart she came
E♭
B♭
E♭
On - ly to fly a - way,
A♭
E♭7
A♭
On - ly to fly as day
cresc.
F7
B♭
Fm7/B♭
B♭7
flies from moon - light.
f
dim. e poco rit.

E♭
Fm7
E♭/G
E♭/B♭
B♭/D
Now, now I'm a - lone,
Still
mp a tempo
D♭dim
A♭/C
A♭m/C♭
E♭/B♭
dream - ing of par - a - dise,
Still
Cm/A
A♭maj7
Cm/A
E♭
say - ing that par - a - dise
Once
f allargando
Fm/B♭
To Coda
E♭
Em6
B♭7
E♭
near - ly was mine.
mine.
a tempo

Verse
D7
Gm
D7♯5
So clear and deep are my fan - cies
D7
Gm
D7sus
D7
Of things I wish were true. I'll
Gm
Cm/A
D7
G
keep re - mem - b'ring eve - nings I wish I'd
D+
G
Gm
spent with you. I'll keep re -
mf
mp

D♭13
G♭
mem - b'ring kiss - es
From lips I'll
F13
B♭
nev - er own,
And all the
E♭m
B♭/F
E♭dim/F
love - ly ad - ven - tures
That we have nev - er
f espressivo
mf
B♭
D.S. al Coda
known.
rit.
CODA
E♭
mine.
f

THOROUGHLY MODERN MILLIE

from THOROUGHLY MODERN MILLIE

Words by SAMMY CAHN
Music by JAMES VAN HEUSEN

F/C
G7
C7
heav - en knows, the world has gone to rack and to
F6
F°7
F6
F°7
ruin.
F6
F°7
F6
A7
What we
f
mf
Dm
Dm(maj7)
Dm7
think is chic, u - nique, and quite a - dor - a - ble,

G9
F6/C
Db7b5
they think is odd and Sod - om and Go -
cresc.
C
Db/C
Bb7b5
mor - rah - ble!
f
A7 N.C.
D
But the fact is ev - 'ry - thing to - day is thor - ough - ly
mf
E9
E13
N.C.
A7
A7/B
mod - ern. (Check your per - son - al - i - ty.) Ev - 'ry - thing to -

C°7
A7/C♯
D7
D9
N.C.
day makes yes - ter - day slow.
(Bet - ter face re - al - i - ty.)
G
Gm6
D
F♯7/C♯
It's not in - san - i - ty,
says *Van - i - ty*
Bm
E13
F♯m
G°
E7/G♯
Fair.
In fact,
it's styl - ish to
N.C.
A7
A°7
A7
A°7
raise your skirts and bob your hair,
Raise your skirts and bob your hair,
Raise your skirts and

F9 E9 A7 D6
bob your hair!
bob your hair!
Have you seen the way they kiss in the
E9 E13 N.C. A7
movies? (Is - n't it de - lect - a - ble?) Paint - ing lips and
N.C. F♯13 N.C.
pen - cil - lin - ing your brow now is quite re - spect - a - ble.
G Gm6 D
Good - bye, good good - y girl, I'm chang - ing, and
3
3

B9
Em7
A
Em7
A7
Em7
A7
Em7
how. So beat the drums 'cause here comes Thor - ough - ly Mod - ern
G/A
A7
D6
B♭7
D
B°7
Mil - lie now!
F♯7
Bm
Bm(maj7)
What we think is chic, u - nique, and quite a -
Bm7
E9
Bm
dor - a - ble, they think is odd and

E7
A
Sod - om and Go - mor - rah - ble! But the fact is,

F N.C.
G9
ev - 'ry - thing to - day is thor - ough - ly mod - ern.
mp

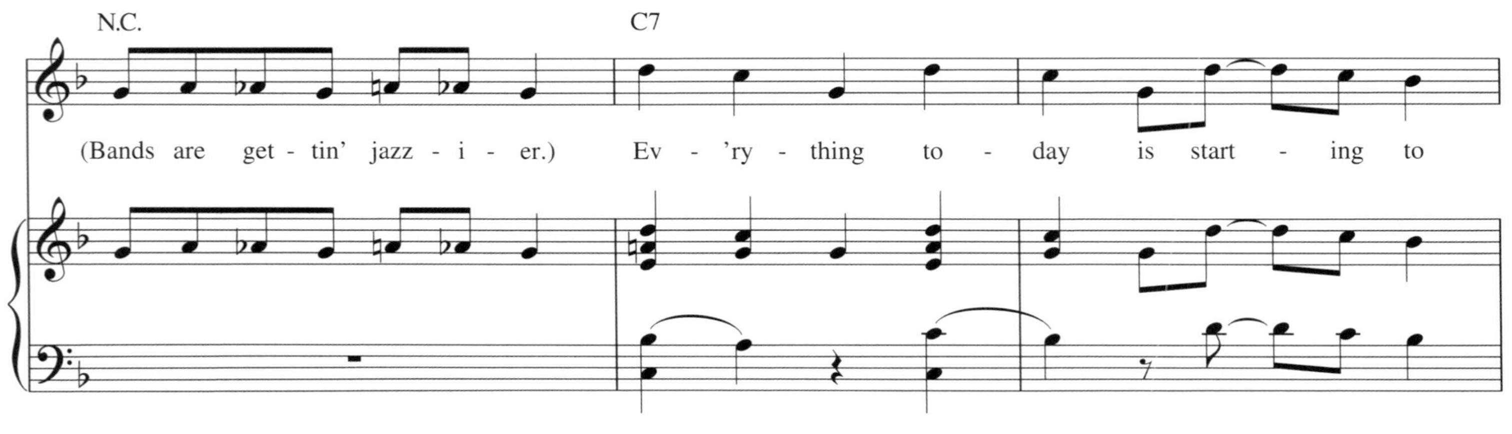
N.C.
C7
(Bands are get - tin' jazz - i - er.) Ev - 'ry - thing to - day is start - ing to

N.C.
F13
N.C.
B6
go. (Cars are get - tin' snaz - zi - er.) Men say
mf

B♭m
F/C
A7
Dm
it's crim - i - nal what wom - en - 'll do.
G9
N.C.
C7
What they're for - get - ting is this is nine - teen
twen - ty - two!
F
f
G7
Am7
B♭m6
G7/B
C9

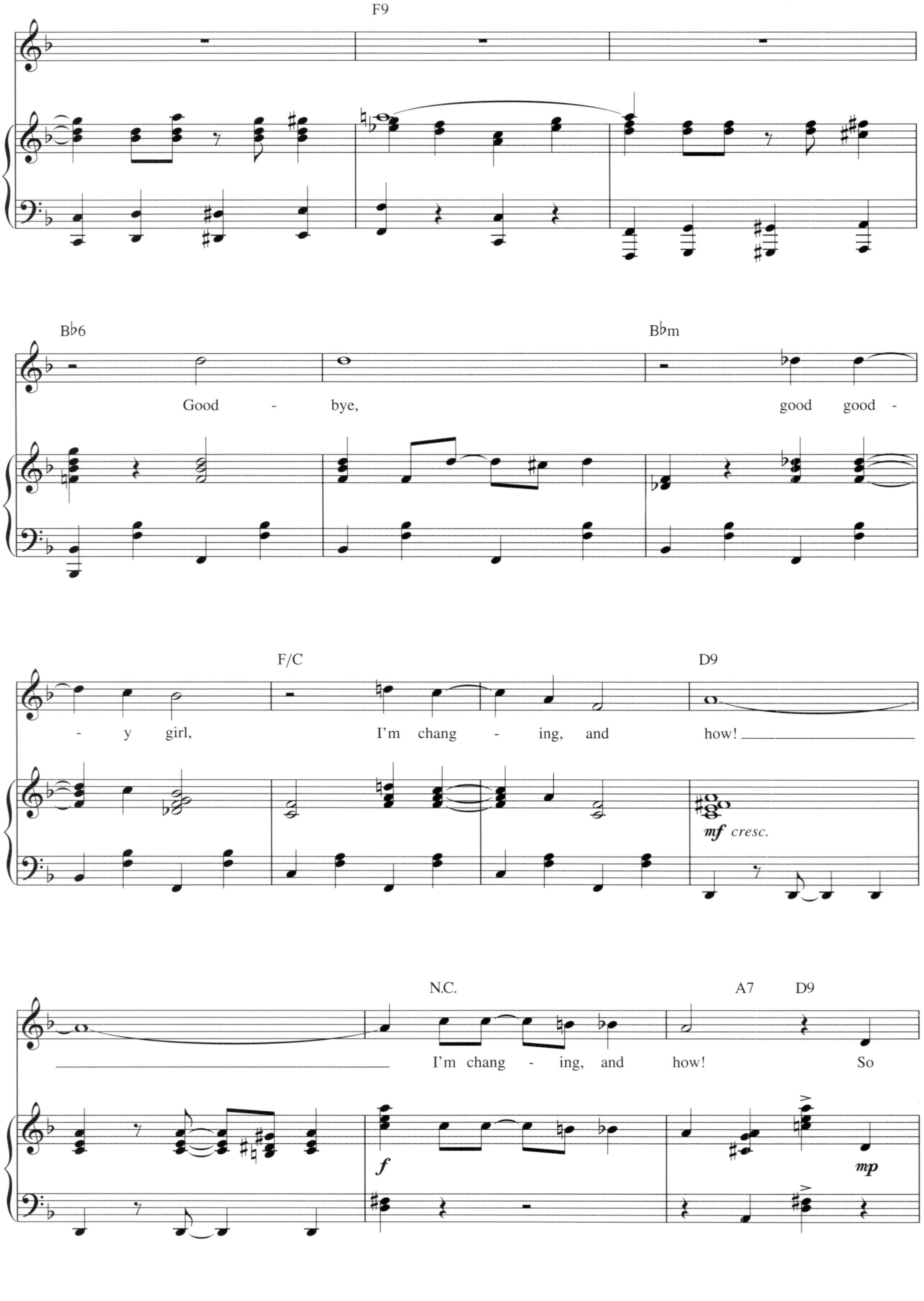

F9

Bb6 Bbm

Good - bye, good good -

F/C D9

- y girl, I'm chang - ing, and how!

mf cresc.

N.C.
beat the drums 'cause here comes thor - ough - ly Hot off the press! One step
grad. cresc.
a - head! Jazz Age! Whoop - ee, ba - by! We're so Thor - ough - ly
Gm7
N.C.
Mod - ern
Mil - lie
f
R.H.
gliss.
F
D♭7
F6
now!
ff
gliss.
gliss.

TILL THERE WAS YOU

from MEREDITH WILLSON'S THE MUSIC MAN

By MEREDITH WILLSON

Fm7
Abm6
Eb
Gbdim
nev - er saw them wing - ing, No, I nev - er saw them at
Fm7
Bb7b9
Eb6
Abmaj7
Ebmaj9
all till there was you. And there was
p
Ab
Adim
Eb
mu - sic and there were won - der - ful ros - es, they
mf
C7
C7#5
Fm7
F7
tell me in sweet fra - grant mead - ows of
dim.

Bb7
Bb7#5
Bb7b9
Eb
dawn, and dew, There was love all a -
8va
mp
p
Edim
Fm7
Abm6
round, but I nev - er heard it sing - ing, No, I
Eb
Gbdim
Fm7
Bb7b9
1
Eb6
Abmaj7
nev - er heard it at all till there was you.
3
Ebmaj9
2
Eb6
Abmaj9
Ebmaj13
And there was you.
molto rit.
pp

UNEXPECTED SONG
from SONG AND DANCE

Music by ANDREW LLOYD WEBBER
Lyrics by DON BLACK

Gently (♩ = 76)

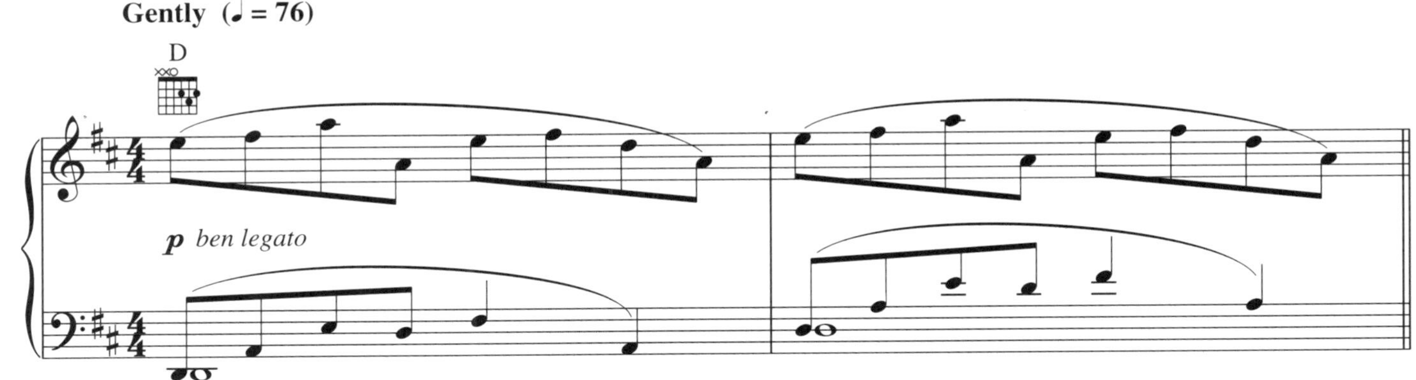

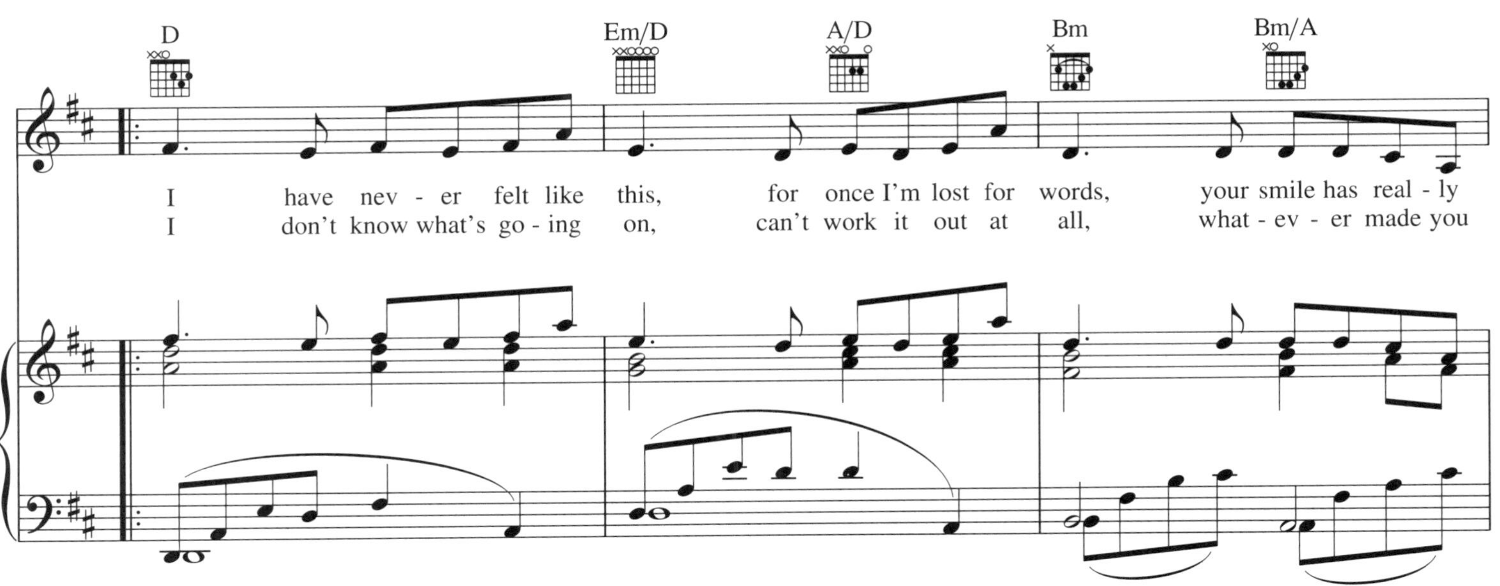

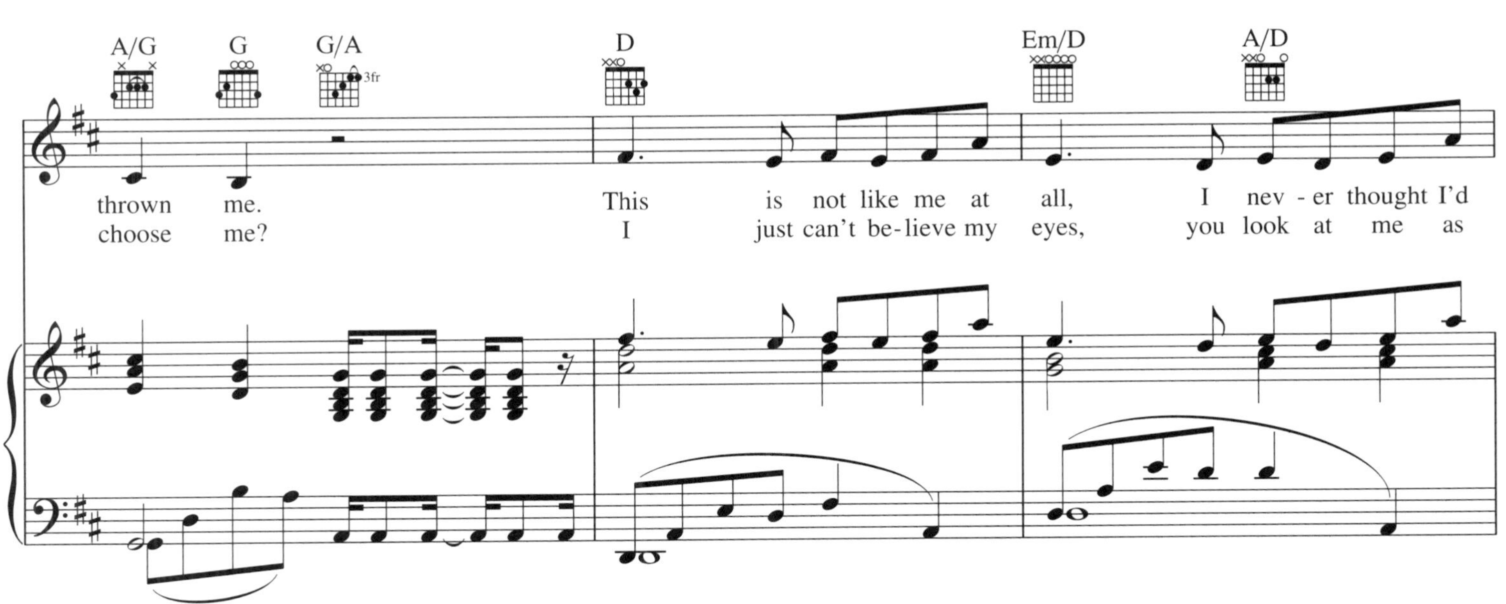

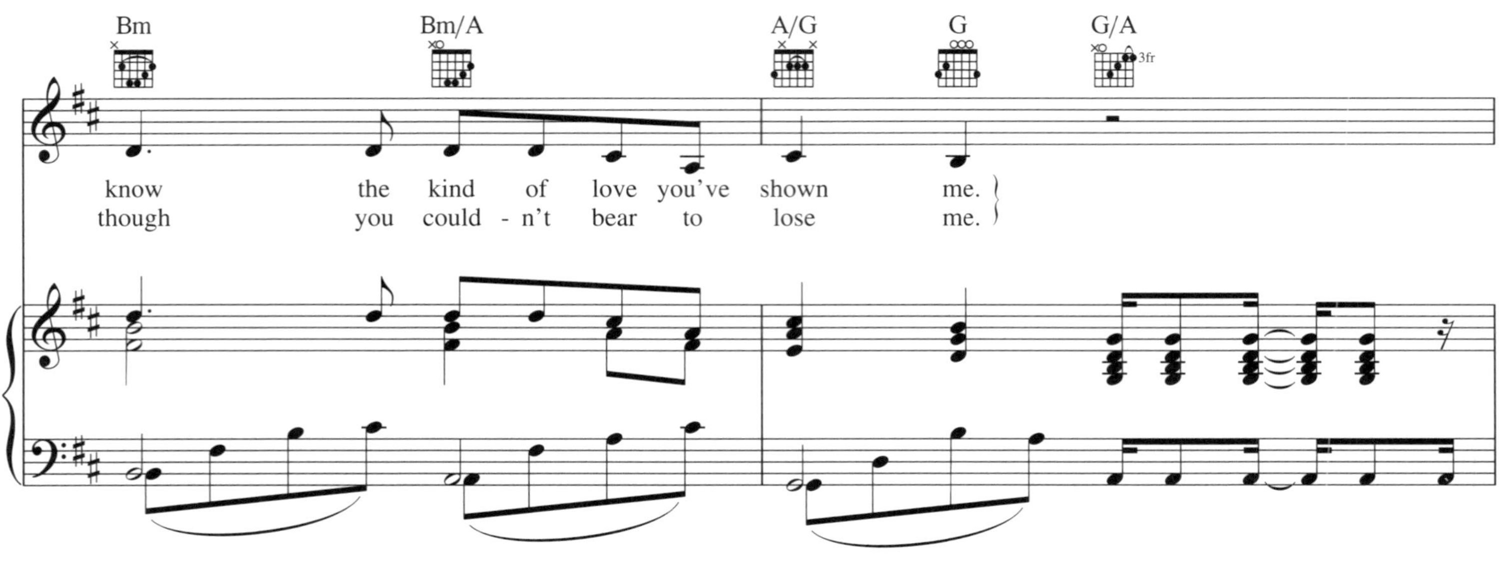
Bm
Bm/A
A/G
G
G/A
3fr
know the kind of love you've shown me.
though you could - n't bear to lose me.

D
D7
G
Now, no mat - ter where I am, no mat - ter what I do, I see your face ap -

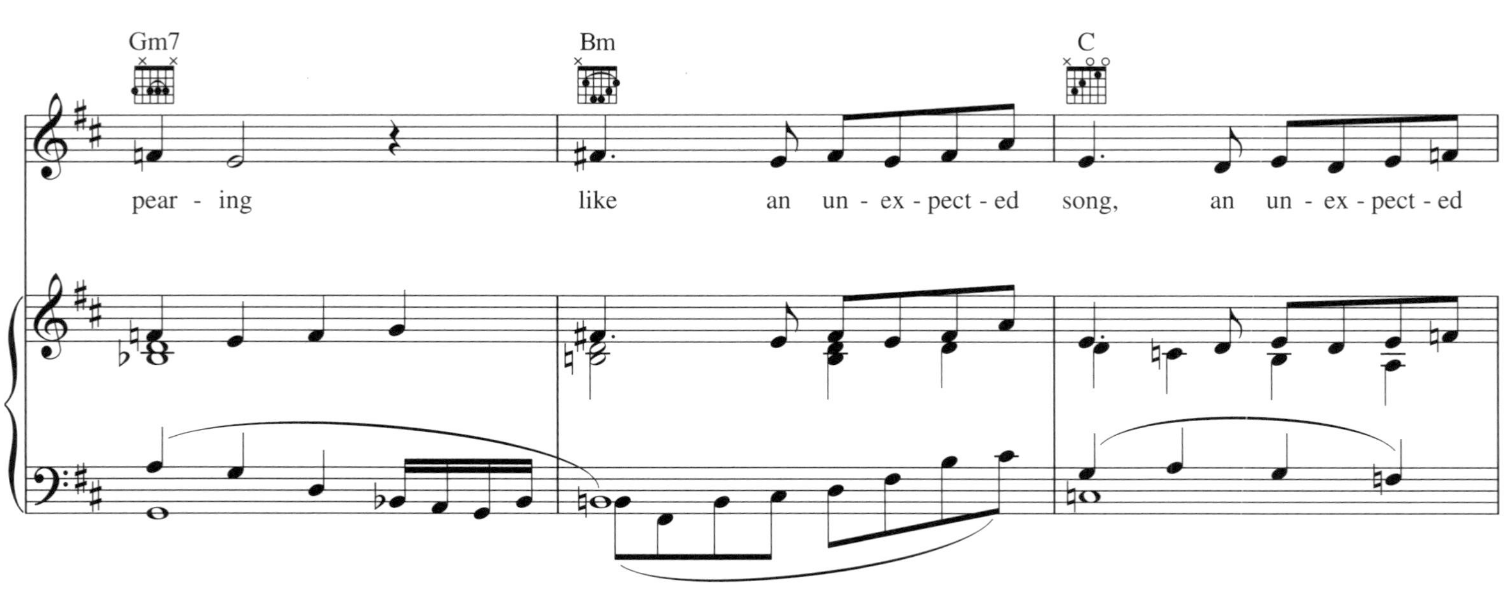
Gm7
Bm
C
pear - ing like an un - ex - pect - ed song, an un - ex - pect - ed

F
1
D
2
D
song that on-ly we are hear - ing.
hear - ing.
rit. e. cresc.
G
Am/G
D/G
I have nev - er felt like this, for once I'm lost for
f a tempo
Em
Em/D
D/C
C
C/D
G
words, your smile has real - ly thrown me. This is not like me at

Am/G
D/G
Em
Em/D
D/C
C
C/D
all, I nev - er thought I'd know the kind of love you've shown me.

G
G7
C
Now, no mat - ter where I am, no mat - ter what I do, I see your face ap -

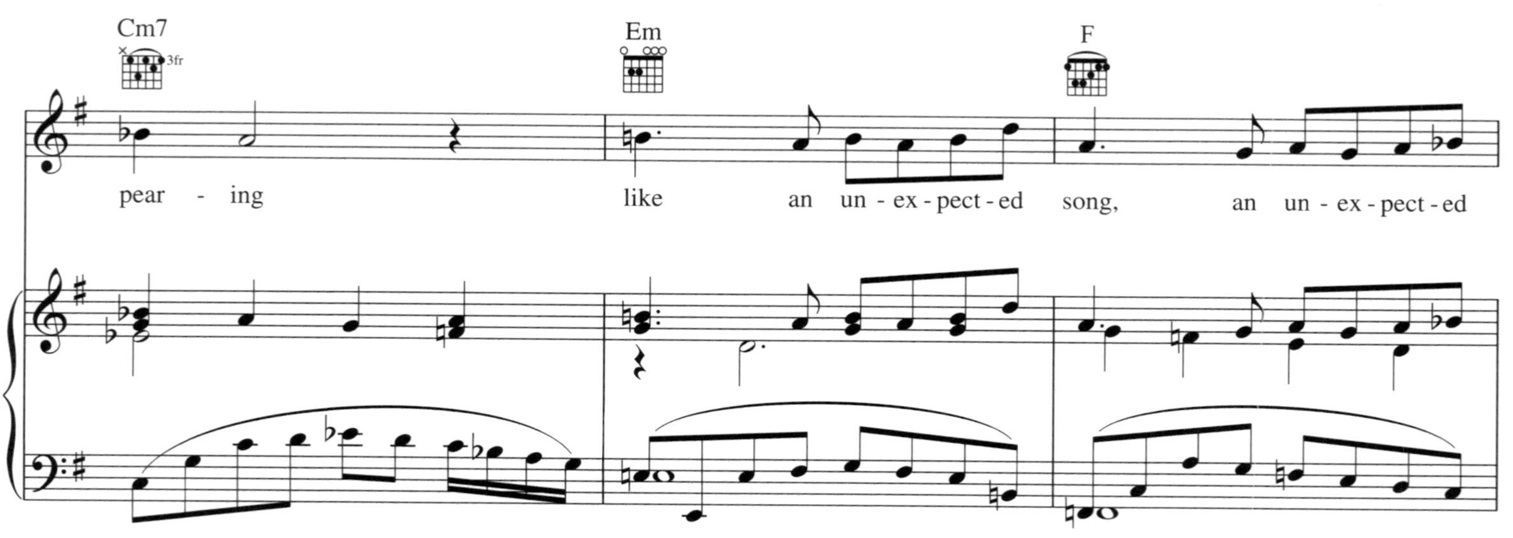
Cm7
3fr
Em
F
pear - ing like an un - ex - pect - ed song, an un - ex - pect - ed

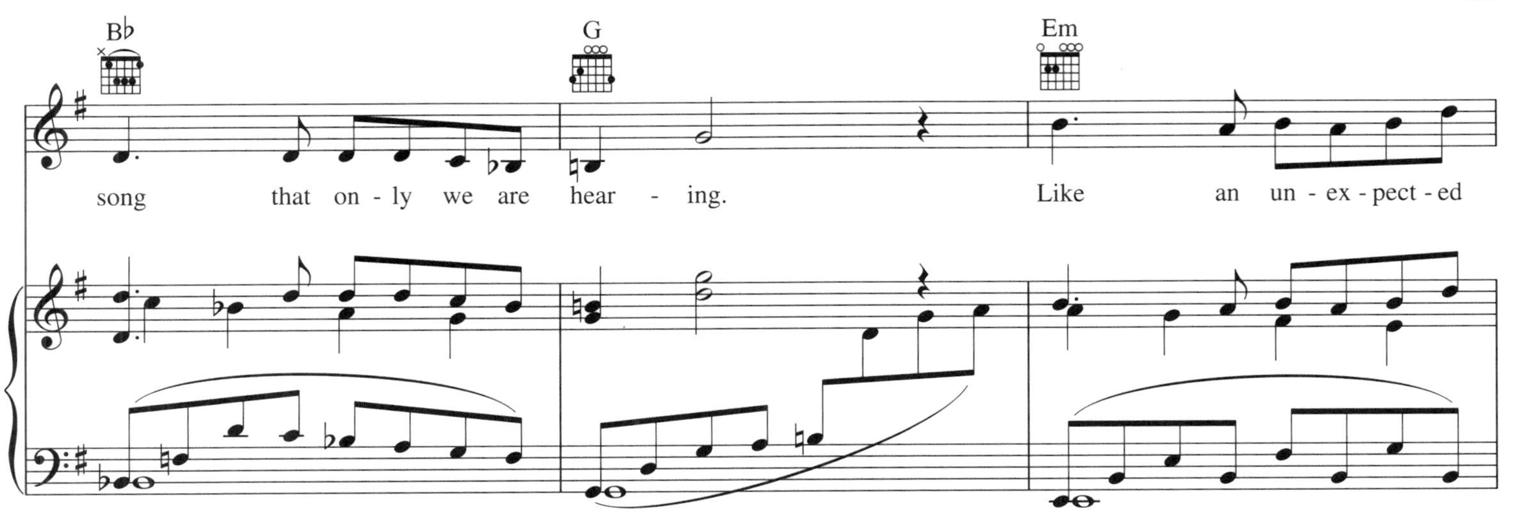
B♭
G
Em
song that on - ly we are hear - ing. Like an un - ex - pect - ed

F
B♭
G
song, an un - ex - pect - ed song that on - ly we are hear - ing.
ff

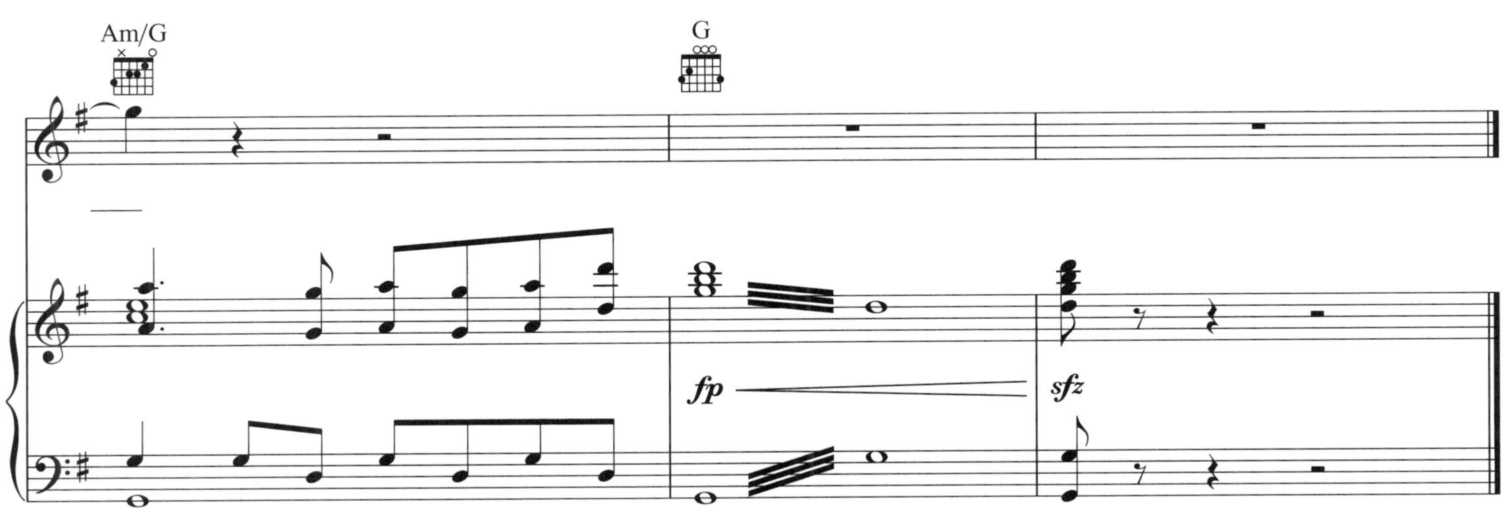
Am/G
G
fp
sfz

TOO CLOSE FOR COMFORT

from the Musical MR. WONDERFUL

Words and Music by JERRY BOCK, LARRY HOLOFCENER and GEORGE WEISS

Moderately
E/B A/B B7 E
a wom-an and man in love.
Since
Am7 D7
I can - not con - sult a book of
G Am7 D7 G
knowl - edge that may be ly - ing on a shelf,
I
Not too slowly, with a beat
B♭7 E♭ Dm7
guess I'll have a con - fi - den - tial dis - cus - sion with my - self.
3fr
G7
Passionately
C6
Be wise, be

Cm6
3fr
Gm6
3fr
A7
smart, be - have, my heart. Don't up -
Fm6
G7
C6
Cmaj7
set your cart when {she's he's} so close.
C7
C6
Cm6
3fr
Be soft, be sweet, but
Gm6
3fr
A7
Fm6
G7
be dis - creet. Don't go off your beat. {She's He's} too

C
C6
C+
F6
F7
close for com - fort, too close, too
Fm6
C
C7
close for com - fort. Please, not a - gain.
F6
F7
Fm6
A♭7
4fr
Too close, too close to know just when to say when.
G7
C6
Cm6
3fr
Gm6
3fr
Be firm, be fair, be sure, be -

A7
Fm6
G7
C
ware. On your guard, take care while there's such temp -
C6
C+
F6
F7
Fm6
ta - tion. One thing leads to an - oth - er,
Cm6
3fr
D7
A♭9
4fr
G9
9fr
too late to run for cov - er.
She's
He's
much too
To Coda
G7♭9
Cm7
3fr
D7
G7
D.S. al Coda
close for com - fort now!
Be

CODA
Cm7
3fr
now!
Too
close,
Cm6
3fr
too
close.
A♭9
4fr
G9
9fr
G7♭9
Cm
3fr
Cm/B♭
8fr
She's
He's
much
too
close
for
com
-
fort
now!
F7/A
3fr
A♭7
4fr
Cm/G
3fr
A♭/G♭
4fr
F7
D♭7♭5
8fr
Cm
3fr
sfz

UNUSUAL WAY
(In A Very Unusal Way)
from NINE

Words and Music by
MAURY YESTON

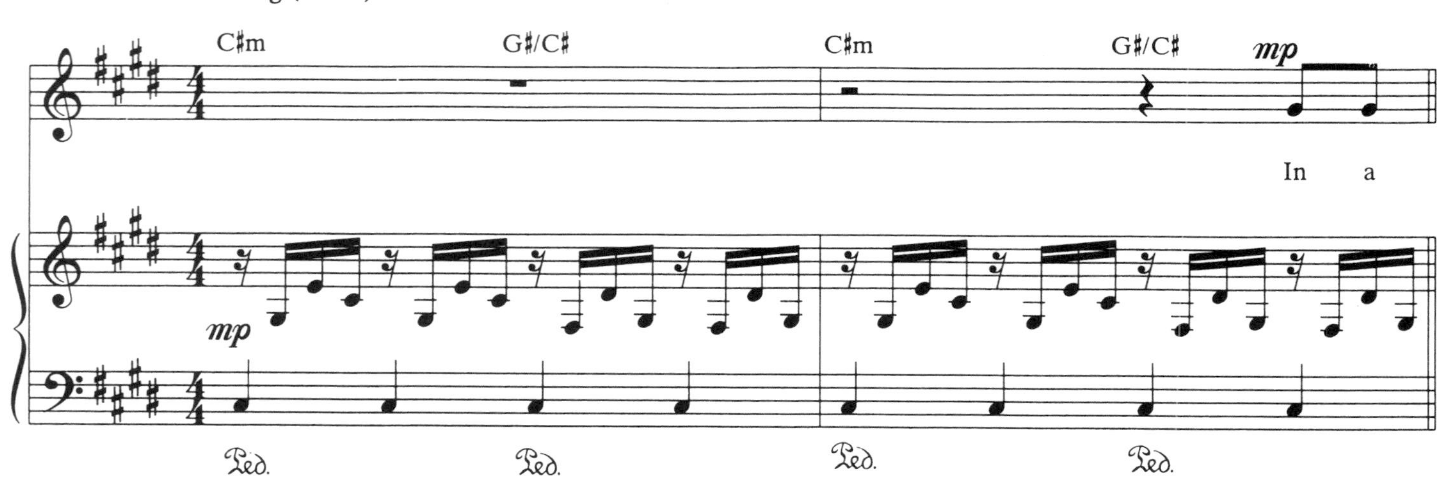

C♯m
C♯m/B
F♯/A♯
F♯m/A
G♯7
C♯m
C♯m/B
May - be it last - ed a day,
may - be it last - ed an hour,
Some- thing in- side me goes weak,
some- thing in- side me sur- ren - ders,
1.
A
D
Bm7/E
Em7/A
but some-how it will nev - er end...
In a
2.
A
D
Bm7/E
E7
E/D
C♯m
C♯m/B
F♯m/A
and you're the rea - son why,
you're the rea-son why.
D♯m7/G♯
Ped.

F♯/G♯
E♯m/G♯
You don't know what you do to me,
L.H.
R.H.
5
✻ Ped.
you don't have a clue.
You can't tell what it's like to be
me, look - ing at you.
It

F♯/G♯ A♯m F♯ D♯m7/G♯ G♯7
scares me so___ that I can hard-ly speak. In a
C♯m G♯7/D♯ C♯m/E C♯7/E♯ F♯m F♯m/G♯
ver-y un-u - su-al way I owe_ what I am___ to you._ Though at
F♯m F♯m/E B7/D♯ B7 E E/D♯ G♯/D♯
times it ap-pears__ I won't stay, I nev - er__ go.
C♯m C♯m/B F♯/A♯ F♯m/A G♯7 C♯m C♯m/B
Spe-cial to me in my life since the first day__ that I met___ you,

A
A/C♯
D
B7/D♯
E
how could I ev - er for-get you once you had touched my soul?
G♯7/D♯
C♯m
C♯m/B
F♯/A♯
In a ver-y un-u - su-al way
F♯m/A
A/G♯
D♯m7/G♯
you've made me
C♯
F♯/C♯
C♯
F♯/C♯
rit.
C♯
whole.
rit.

WHAT KIND OF FOOL AM I?

from the Musical Production STOP THE WORLD–I WANT TO GET OFF

Words and Music by LESLIE BRICUSSE
and ANTHONY NEWLEY

Moderately slow

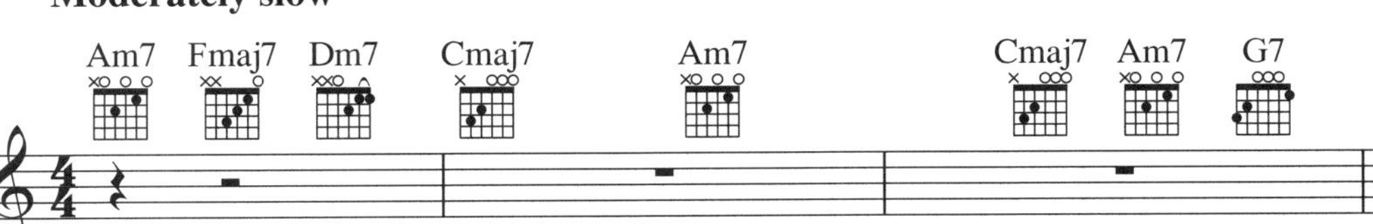

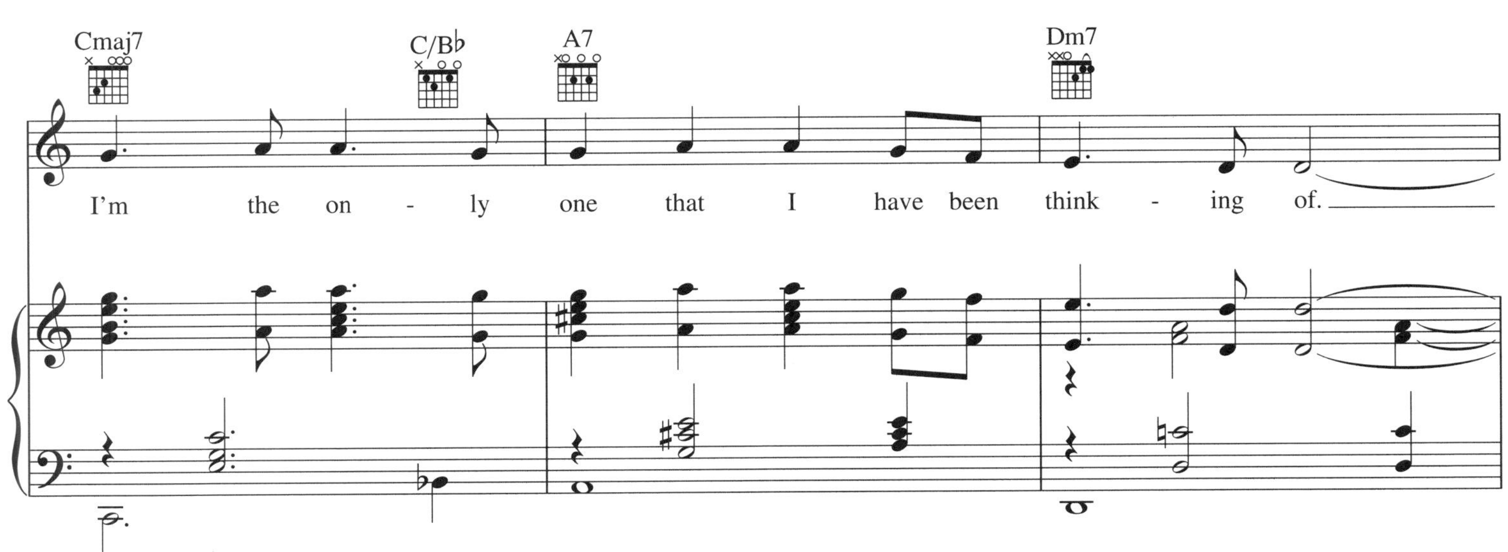

Dm7/G
G7
C
Am7
What kind of man is this? An empty
life
D7
G/B
Em7
Am7
D7
shell, a lonely cell in which an empty heart must
Gsus
3fr
G7
Cmaj7
dwell. What kind of lips are these that lied with
clown am I? What do I
Dm7(add4)
3fr
G7
Cmaj7
ev'ry kiss? That whispered empty words of
know of life? Why can't I cast away the

Gm/B♭
A7
Gm7
C7
love that left me a - lone like this?
mask of play and live my life?
Why can't I
Why can't I
F6
Dm7♭5
C/E
fall in love like an - y oth - er man
fall in love 'til I don't give a damn
D7
Dm7
Fm
G7♭9
and may - be then I'll know what kind of fool I
1
C
Cmaj7
Am7
Fmaj7
Fmaj7/G
F/G
G7
am.
What kind of
2
C
Cmaj7
Am7
Fmaj7
Dm7
Cmaj7
am.

WHAT I DID FOR LOVE

from A CHORUS LINE

Music by MARVIN HAMLISCH
Lyric by EDWARD KLEBAN

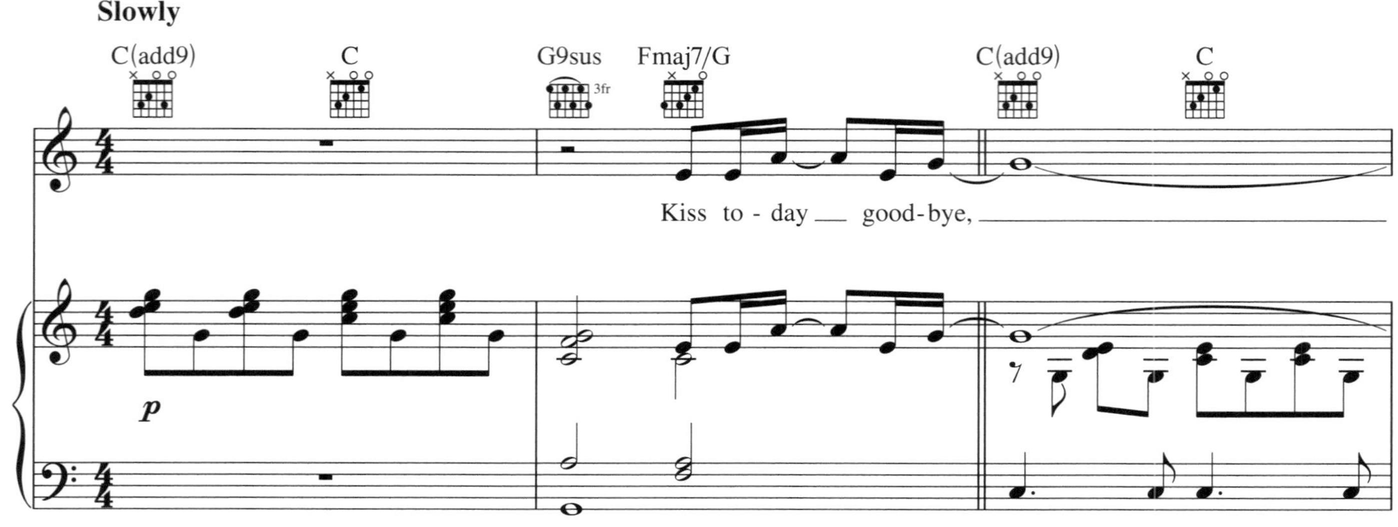

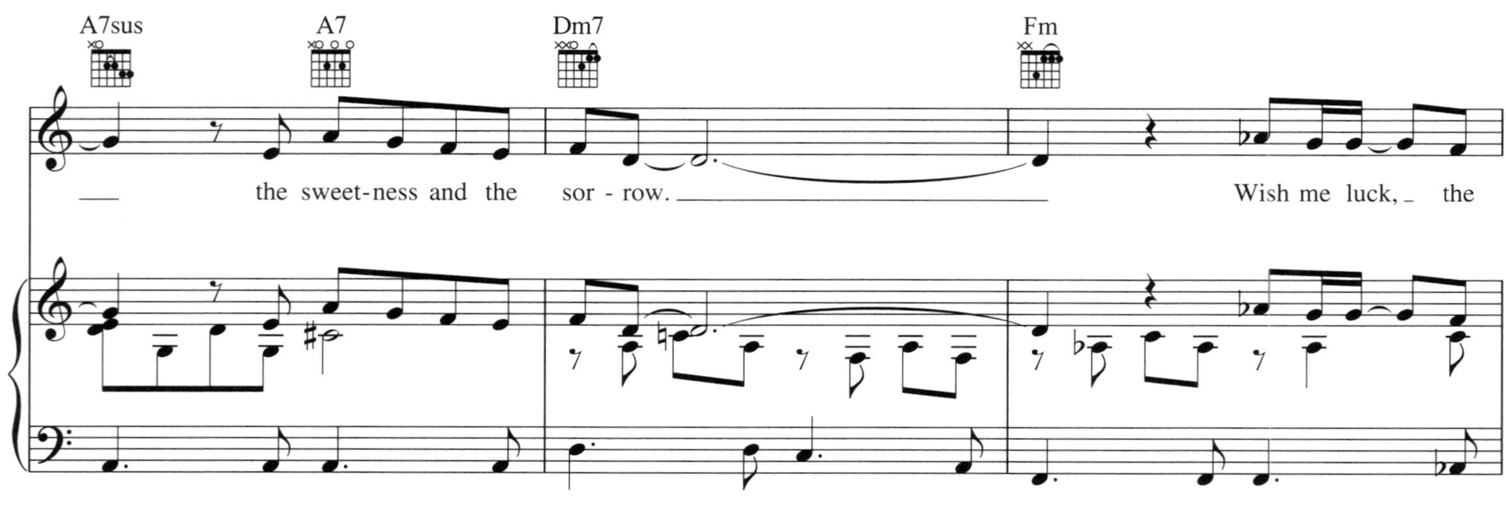

Fm
Dm7♭5
G
G/F
what I did for love,
what I did for love.
G
N.C.
C(add9)
C
A7sus
A7
Look, my eyes are dry.
The gift was ours to
Dm7
Fm
C
G/B
bor-row.
It's as if we al-ways
D9
4fr
N.C.
Fm
knew.
And I won't for-get
what I did for love,

Dm7♭5 G G/F Em7 G/D Am Am/G

what I did for love. Gone,

Fmaj7 E7sus E7 Am Am/G F♯m7♭5 B7sus B7

love is nev - er gone. As we trav - el

Em G/A A7 Dm7♭5 G7sus/D

on, love's what we'll re - mem - ber.

G7 N.C. C(add9) C A7sus A7

Kiss to - day good - bye, and point me t'ward to -

Dm7 Fm C G/B

mor - row. We did what we had to

Am Am/G D7/F♯ Am7/E D7 F C/E

do. Won't for - get, can't re - gret what I did

Dm7 G7sus G7 C C/B♭ Fm/A♭ N.C.

for love... what I did for

C C/B♭ Fm/A♭ N.C. C

love what I did for love.

rall.

WHEN DID I FALL IN LOVE

from the Musical FIORELLO!

Words by SHELDON HARNICK
Music by JERRY BOCK

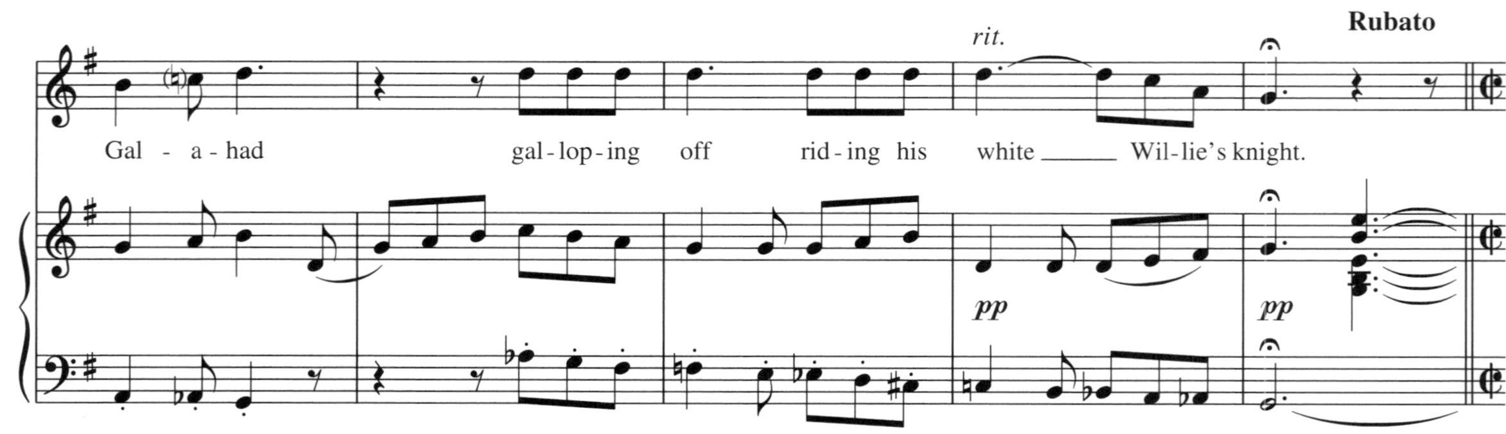

Out of the house ten sec-onds and I miss him, I miss him more
with each good - bye. Out of the house ten sec - onds and I miss him,
and no one's more as - ton-ished than I. I nev - er
Rubato
once pre - tend-ed that I loved him; when did I start this change of
pp
p
p
(mp)
(pp)

Slowly and tenderly
heart?
When did I fall in love?
What night?
Which day?
pp
When did I first be - gin to feel this way?
(pp)
How could the
(pp)
mo - ment pass, un - felt, ig - nored?
3
Where was the blind - ing flash?
3
Where was the crash - ing chord?
f
(pp)
When did I fall in love?
I can't
pp
p
(pp)

re - call,
not that it
mat - ters
at
all.
pp
pp
cresc.
f
rit.
It does - n't
mat - ter when
or why
or how,
as long as
L.H.
L.H.
L.H.
L.H.
rit.
ten.
I love
him
now.
When did re - spect
first be-come af - fec - tion?
When did af - fec - tion

3
sud-den-ly soar?
3
What a strange and beau-ti-ful touch
(p)
p
that I love him so much,
when I did-n't be-fore.
pp
8
mf
(p)
When did I fall in love?
Which night?
Which day?
When did I
p
p
first be-gin to feel this way?
How could the mo-ment pass,
un-felt,
pp
p
8
8
cresc.
8

ig - nored? Where was the blind - ing flash? Where was the crash - ing chord?
cresc.
f
When did I fall in love? I can't re - call, not that it
p
pp
mat - ters at all. I'm where I want to be, his love,
p
cresc.
f
L.H.
L.H.
L.H.
rit.
ten.
his wife un - til the end of my life.
(L.H.)
L.H.
rit.
ff

WHEN WILL SOMEONE HEAR?

from MARTIN GUERRE

Music by CLAUDE-MICHEL SCHÖNBERG
Lyrics by ALAIN BOUBLIL and STEPHEN CLARK

A
D
Em/D
D
Em/D
When will some - one hear?
Love that once was close,
faith that once was clear.
Bm
Em7
A
F♯/A♯
Now all I've known and all I've loved is
all I have to grieve.
All that I've be - gun,
F♯7/A♯
Bm
G
D/F♯
A
all that I be - lieve
is just an - oth - er bro - ken dream.
When will some - one
D
E7
A/E
F♯
Bm/F♯
hear?
They seem so strong,
they seem so sure.

G
C/G
A
D/A
G
F♯m7
They'd take my soul and still want more.
No one here will lis - ten, it's not
Em7
B/D♯
4fr
B7
E
F♯m/E
me they're fight - ing for.
Now I know.
Don't de - cide for me.
E
F♯m/E
C♯m
4fr
Now at last it's clear,
and don't think I'm that lit - tle girl they
F♯m7
B
G♯/B♯
6fr
want - ed me to be.
They don't know me now,

G♯7/B♯
C♯m
4fr
A
E/G♯
fight - ing to be free. There's no one here to un - der - stand. _
3
B
C♯m
4fr
F♯m
E/G♯
When will some - one hear? I will car - ry on,
A
E/B
A
E/G♯
B7
till the fear has gone. Till the day I find... there's some - one who will
E
A/E
E
A/E
E
hear.
3
3

WHERE IS LOVE?

from the Broadway Musical OLIVER!

Words and Music by
LIONEL BART

Dm7 G7 C Dm7/A G7 Cmaj7 C6
of? Where is she
Cmaj7 Dm7 G7 Cmaj7 C7 F Cm7 F7
who I close my eyes to see? Will I ev - er know the
B♭maj7 B♭m7 E♭7 A♭maj7 A♭ Dm7 G7
sweet "hel - lo" that's meant for on - ly me?
C Dm7/A G7 Cmaj7 C6 F G7
Who can say where she may hide? Must I trav - el far and
Ev - 'ry night I kneel and pray. Let to - mor - row be the

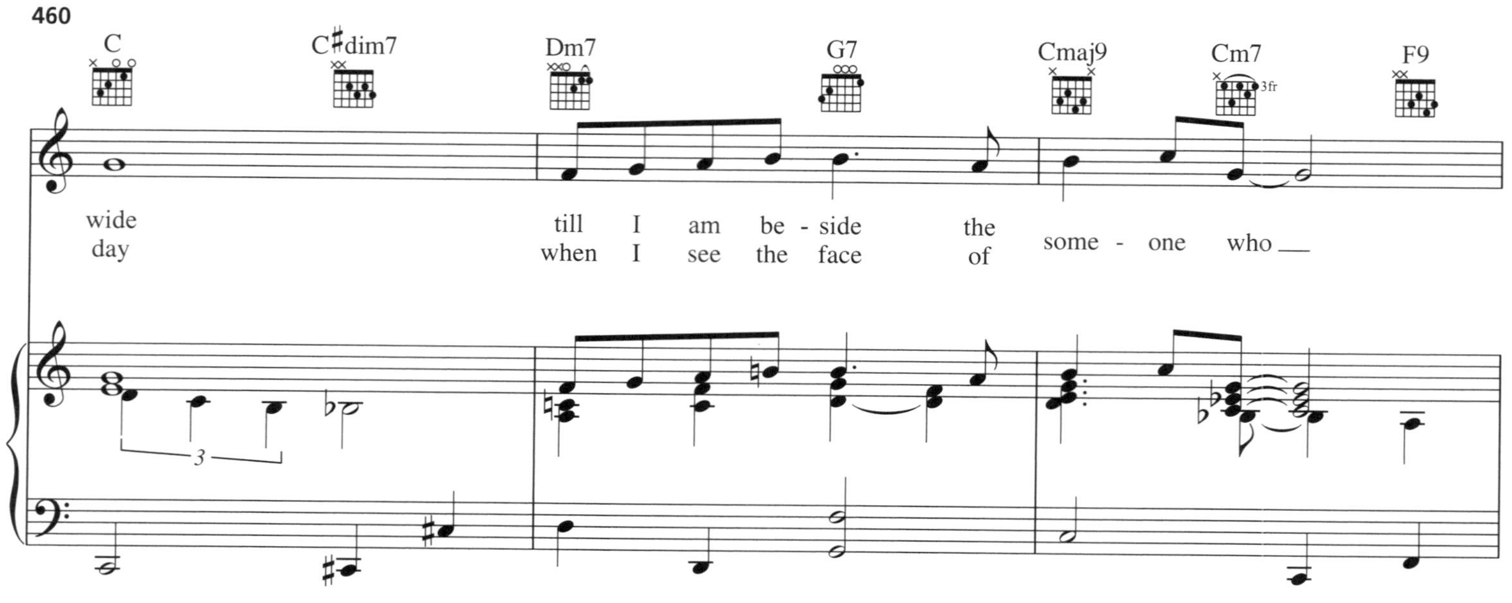
C
C♯dim7
Dm7
G7
Cmaj9
Cm7
3fr
F9
wide
day
till I am be - side the
when I see the face of
some - one who
3

B♭maj7
B♭6
Amaj7
C♯dim7
A7
Dm7
Am
Dm7
F/G
G7♭9
I can mean
some - thing to?
Where,
where
is

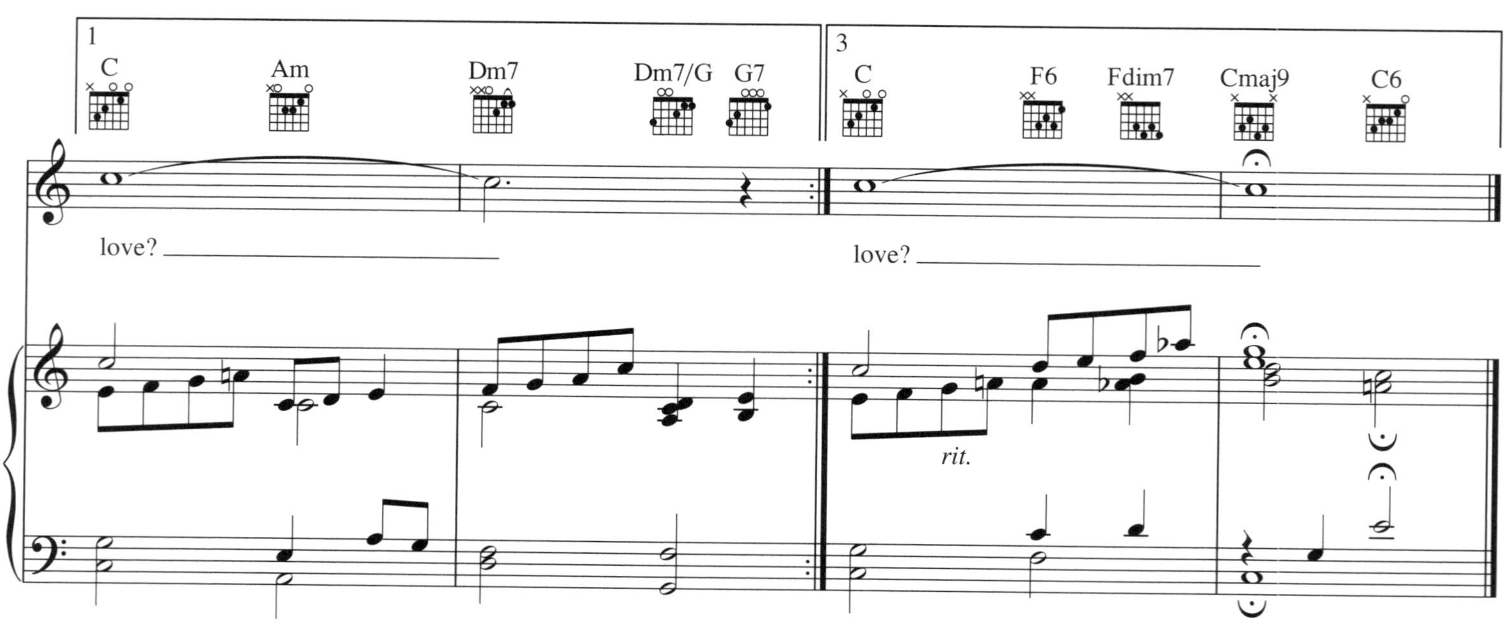
1
C
Am
Dm7
Dm7/G
G7
3
C
F6
Fdim7
Cmaj9
C6
love?
love?
rit.

WHO CAN I TURN TO
(When Nobody Needs Me)
from THE ROAR OF THE GREASEPAINT—THE SMELL OF THE CROWD

Words and Music by LESLIE BRICUSSE
and ANTHONY NEWLEY

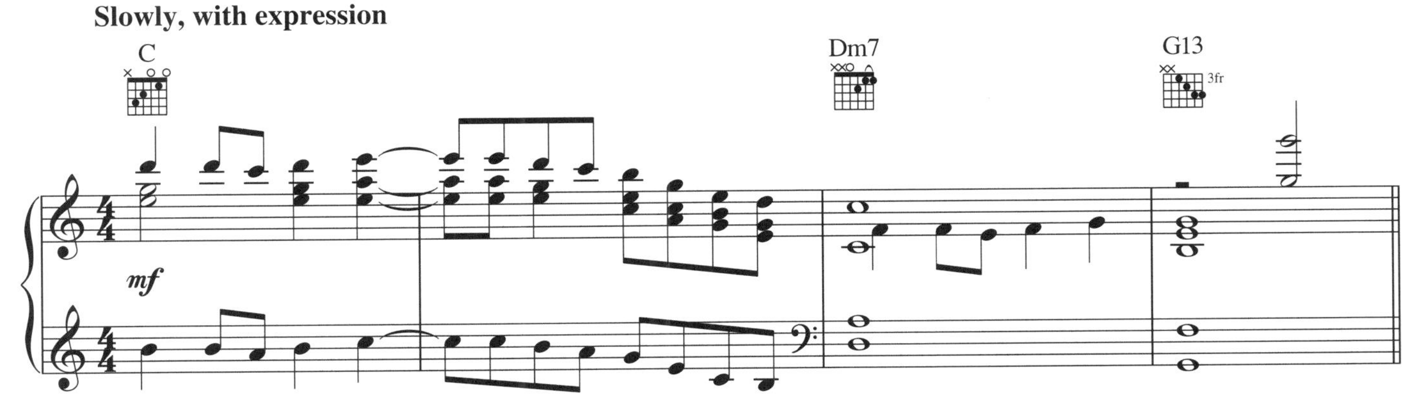

C9 F F6 Fmaj7 F Em7 Cmaj7/E
With no star to guide me, and no one be - side me,
Am Am/G Fmaj7 Dm6/F Em7 A7
I'll go on my way, and af - ter the day, the
Dm Dm7 G7 Cmaj9 C6
dark - ness will hide me. And may - be to - mor - row I'll
Dm7 G7 Dm7 G7/D C C6
find what I'm af - ter. I'll throw off my sor - row,

Cmaj7
C
Gm
3fr
Gm7
C9
beg, steal or bor - row my share of laugh - ter.
With
F
F+
Dm6/F
E7
Am
Am(maj7)
Am7/G
5fr
you I could learn to,
with you on a new day,
but
F
C6/E
Dm7
D♭7♯9
3fr
1
C6
Dm7/C
G13
3fr
who can I turn to if you turn a - way?
2
C6
Dm7/C
G13
3fr
Cmaj7
C6/9
way?
rit.

WHERE OR WHEN

from BABES IN ARMS

Words by LORENZ HART
Music by RICHARD RODGERS

A♭
Fm7
Fm7♭5
Fm7/B♭
B♭7
E♭
Things you do come back to you, as though they knew the way. Oh, the
Fm
B♭7
E♭
E♭6
tricks your mind can play! It seems we stood and talked like
poco rit.
a tempo
E♭maj7
Fm7
this be - fore. We looked at each oth - er in the same way then,
E♭maj7
E♭6
Fm7♭5
B♭7
but I can't re - mem - ber where or when.

E♭
E♭6
E♭maj7
The clothes you're wear - ing are the clothes you wore. The
Fm7
smile you are smil-ing you were smil - ing then, but I can't re-mem - ber where or
E♭maj7
E♭6
Dm7♭5
G7
Cm
Fm7
when.
Some things that hap - pen for the
G7sus
G7
F/G
G7
Cm
Fm7
first time,
seem to be hap - pen - ing a -

Cm7
F7
Fm7/B♭
B♭7
E♭
E♭6
gain.
And so it seems that we have
E♭maj7
G+
A♭6
B♭6
met be - fore, and laughed be - fore, and
A♭6
Gm
Fm
B♭7
loved be - fore, but who knows where or
1
E♭
Fm/E♭
E♭maj7
Fm/E♭
B♭7sus
B♭7
when!
2
E♭
A♭m7
E♭
when!
rit.

WHY WAS I BORN?

from SWEET ADELINE

Lyrics By OSCAR HAMMERSTEIN II
Music by JEROME KERN

side me, I pic - ture the pret - ti - est sto - ries on - ly to
F7
Bb
wake up, All by my - self.
D
F7
What is the good of me, by my - self?
L.H.
poco rit.
Bb
Bb/D
C#dim7
Edim7
F7/C
F
Why was I born? Why am I
p
a tempo
con pedale

E♭/G F7/A Gm/A Gm B♭/F Em7♭5 E♭6 E♭6/G
liv - ing? What do I get? What am I
F7/A F7 B♭ B♭/D E♭maj7
giv - ing? Why do I want a thing I dare - n't hope for?
sostenuto
Ped.
F7 B♭7 E♭ E♭m(maj7) E♭m6 B♭/D
What can I hope for? I wish I knew.
Cm7 F7 B♭ B♭/D C♯dim7 Edim7 F7/C F7
Why do I try To draw you
con pedale

Eb/G
F7/A
Gm/A
Gm
Bb6/F
E7b5
Eb6
Eb6/G
near me? Why do I cry? You nev - er
F7/A
F7
Bb
Bb6/D
hear me. I'm a poor fool, but what can I
sostenuto
Ped.
C9
Bb/F
C#dim7/F
Cm7/F
F7
do? Why was I born to love
L.H.
3
rall. e dim.
1
Bb
C9/E
F7/Eb
Bb/D
Cm7
F7/C
2
Bb
Eb9
Bb
you?
you?
a tempo
f
morendo
Ped.

WITH A SONG IN MY HEART

from SPRING IS HERE

Words by LORENZ HART
Music by RICHARD RODGERS

Bbm7 Eb7 Ab B
time Ev - 'ry meet - ing's a mar - vel - ous pas - time You're in -
light Not a note of our mu - sic is played out, It will
Eb/Bb Cm Fm7 Bb7 Eb Ab
creas - ing - ly sweet, So when - ev - er we hap - pen to meet
be just as sweet, And an air that I'll live to re - peat:
Eb E7/B Bb7 Bb7#5(b9) Eb Bb7
I greet you With a song in my heart.
rall.
a tempo
Eb Bb7 Eb G7
I be-hold your a - dor - a - ble face, Just a song at the start,
R.H.
4 fr
6 fr
3 fr

Cm
3 fr
G7
Cm
3 fr
Cm/B♭
But it soon is a hymn to your grace.
When the mu - sic
Am7♭5
A♭
4 fr
Fm7
E♭6
D7
swells
I'm touch-ing your
hand;
It tells that you're
cresc.
Fm
D7
G7
C7
Fm
B♭7
E♭
3 fr
stand - ing near,
and
At the sound of your
dim.
p
B♭7
E♭
3 fr
B♭7
voice
Heav-en o - pens its por - tals to me.

E♭
3fr
G7
Cm
3fr
Can I help but re - joice
That a song such as
G7
Cm
3fr
Cm/B♭
Am7♭5
F7
E♭/B♭
6fr
ours came to be?
But I al - ways knew
I would live life
mp
cresc.
F7
E♭/B♭
6fr
A♭6
3fr
B♭7
through
With a song in my heart for
rall.
1
E♭
3fr
E7/B
B♭7
B♭7♯5(♭9)
2
E♭
3fr
you.
you.
a tempo
p

WITH ONE LOOK

from SUNSET BOULEVARD

Music by ANDREW LLOYD WEBBER
Lyrics by DON BLACK and CHRISTOPHER HAMPTON,
with contributions by AMY POWERS

Bm7 D/E E7/D A/C♯ Em7
or the love that you've hun - gered for. When I speak it's with my
A D A/E E7 A E7/A
soul, I can play an - y role. No words can tell the
A E7/A D A/C♯ Bm7 E
sto - ries my eyes tell, watch me when I frown, you can't write that down. You
C G/C C G A F♯m7 A/E
know I'm right, it's there in black and white, when I look your way you'll hear

Bm7
E
A
F♯m
what I say. Yes, with one look I put words to shame,
Bm7
E
E7/D
A/C♯
Em7
just one look sets the screen a - flame. Si - lent mu - sic starts to
A
D
A/C♯
Bm7
E7
play, one tear in my eye makes the whole world cry.
A
F♯m
Bm7
With one look they'll for - give the past, they'll re - joice I've re -
f

D/E E7/D A/C♯ Em/B A/C♯ D

turned at last to my peo - ple in the dark,

A/E E7 A D Bm

still out there in the dark.

f

Em7 G/A A D/F♯ Am

Si - lent mu - sic starts to

p

D G D/F♯ Em7 A

play. With one look you'll know all you need to know.

mf

B/F♯
G♯m
4fr
C♯m
4fr
C♯m/B
With one look I'll ig - nite a blaze, I'll re - turn to my
E/F♯
F♯/E
B/D♯
4fr
F♯m7
B
glo - ry days. They'll say Nor - ma's back at last.
E(add2)
E6
A
This time I am stay - ing, I'm stay - ing for good, I'll be back where I was born to
rit.
Emaj7
E/F♯
B
be, with one look I'll be me.
molto rit.
ff a tempo

YOU'LL NEVER WALK ALONE

from CAROUSEL

Lyrics by OSCAR HAMMERSTEIN II
Music by RICHARD RODGERS

* alternate lyric: hold your head up high

B♭ F Dm

storm is a gold - en sky And the

B♭/D Am/C Gm/B♭ F/A E/G♯ C7/G

sweet sil - ver song of a lark. Walk

mf

F Fdim7 C/E

on through the wind, Walk on through the

cresc.

Fm6 C/G Em

rain, Tho' your dreams be tossed and

dim.

F G7/F C/E E+
blown Walk on, walk on, with
cresc. poco a poco
F D7/F♯ C/G E+ Fmaj7 F♯7♭5
hope in your heart, And you'll nev - er walk a -
f sempre cresc.
Em/G G/F C/E E+ F G9
lone, You'll nev - er walk a -
più cresc.
ff with great expression
9fr
1 C Em Fmaj7 F/G
lone! When you
dim.
mf
2 F Dm/C Em/C C
lone!
allarg.
8vb

WRITTEN IN THE STARS

from Elton John and Tim Rice's AIDA

Music by ELTON JOHN
Lyrics by TIM RICE

Gm
Gm/F
E♭
think of me or speak of me and won - der what be - fell
The
Cm7
Fsus
F
some-one you once loved so long a - go, so well!
D♭
A♭/D♭
G♭/D♭
D♭
F/A
RADAMES:
Nev-er won-der what I'll feel as liv-ing shuf-fles by
B♭m
B♭m/A♭
G♭
A♭sus
A♭
You don't have to ask me and I need not re - ply

D♭
A♭/D♭
G♭/D♭
F/A
Ev - 'ry mo-ment of my life from now un - til I die
B♭m
B♭m/A♭
G♭
E♭m
I will think or dream of you and fail to un-der-stand How a per-fect love can be con-found-ed out
cresc.
A♭sus
A♭
D♭/C
of hand Is it writ-ten in the stars? Are we pay-ing for some crime? Is (that)
f
G♭maj7
Fm/C
all that we are good for just a stretch of mor-tal time? Or some God's ex-per-i-ment In

Bbm
Gbmaj7
Db/F
Ebm7
Absus
Ab
which we have no say?
In which we're giv-en par-a-dise
but on - ly
for a day
A
E/A
D/A
Ab/Eb
Eb
Db/Eb
E
Gb
AIDA:
(Spoken:) Marry the princess, Radames. You can help my people.
This could be our chance to do something important. Don't you see?
sub. p
Ab
Eb/Ab
Db/Ab
Ab
C/E
Noth-ing can be al - tered,
there is noth-ing
to de-cide
No
Fm
Fm/Eb
Db
Db/Eb
es-cape,
no change of heart,
nor an - y place to hide

A♭ G/E
E♭/A♭ D♭/A♭
A♭
C/E
RADAMES:
You are all I'll ev-er want _ but this I am de-nied ____
Fm
Fm/E♭
D♭
Some-times in my dark - est thoughts _ I wish I'd nev-er learned _
RADAMES:
AIDA: What it
B♭m
E♭sus
is to be in love _ and have _ that love ____ re-turned
AIDA:
Is it
D♭(add2)
B♭m7
writ-ten in the stars? _ Are we pay - ing for some crime? ____ Is (that)
sub. p

Gbmaj7
Ebm7
Ab
RADAMES:
AIDA:
all that we are good for just a stretch of mor-tal time? Or some
cresc.
Db
Fm/C
Bbm
Db/Ab
God's ex-per-i-ment In which we have no say? In
f
Gbmaj7
Db/F
Ebm7
Absus
Ab
Db
Ab/Db
Gb/Db
which we're giv-en par-a-dise But on-ly for a day
Db
Ab/Db
Gb/Db
A(add2)
B(add2)
Db
dim.
mp

YOUNGER THAN SPRINGTIME

from SOUTH PACIFIC

Lyrics by OSCAR HAMMERSTEIN II
Music by RICHARD RODGERS

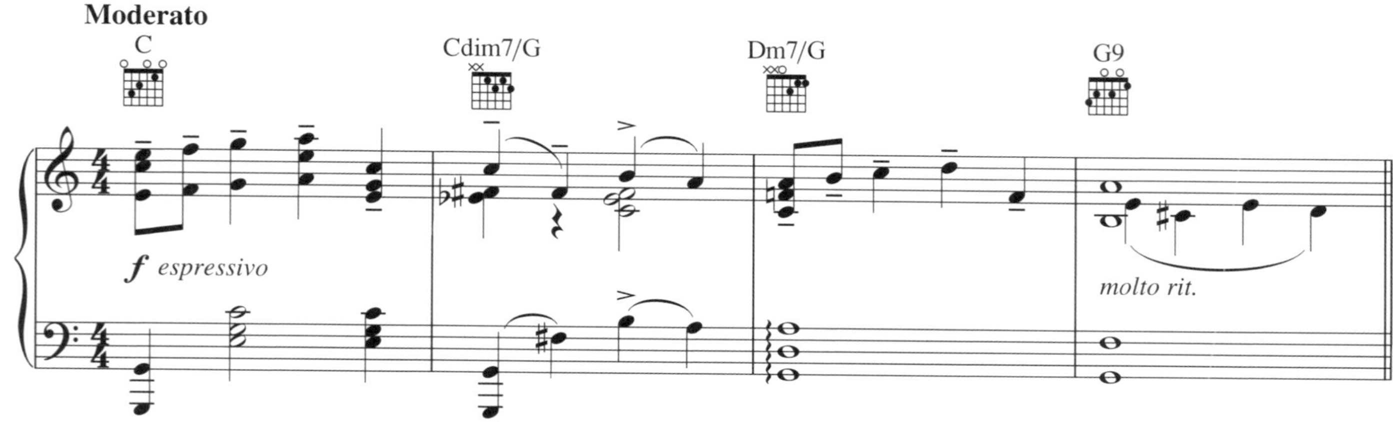

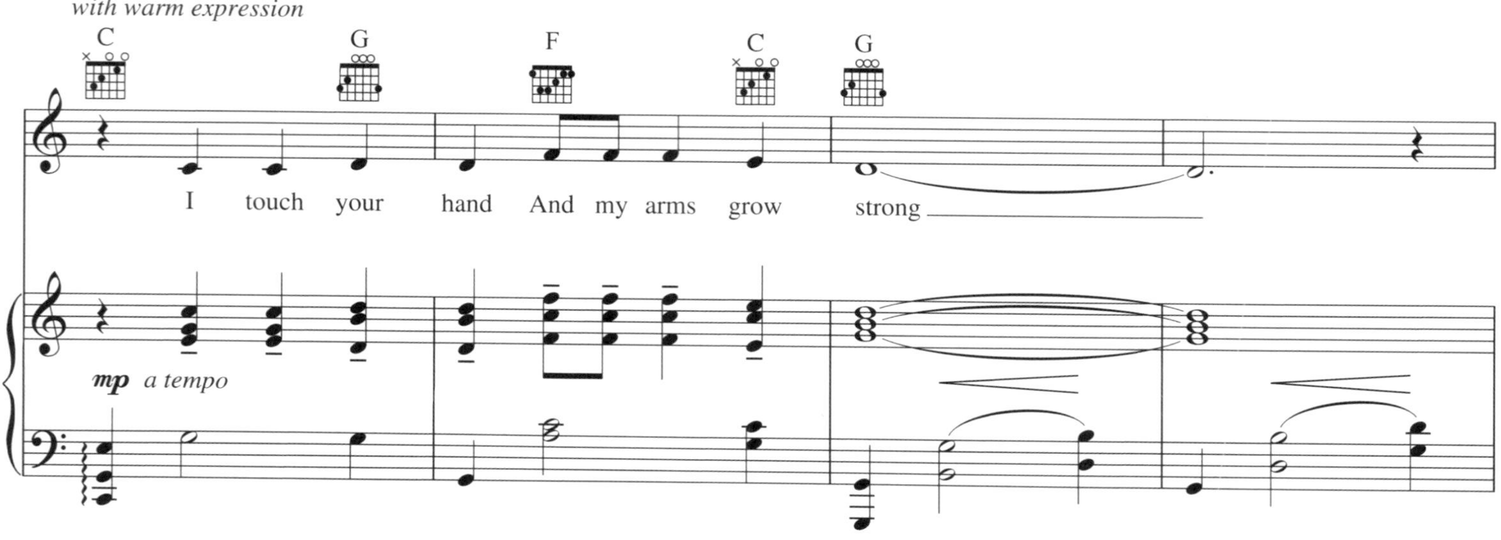

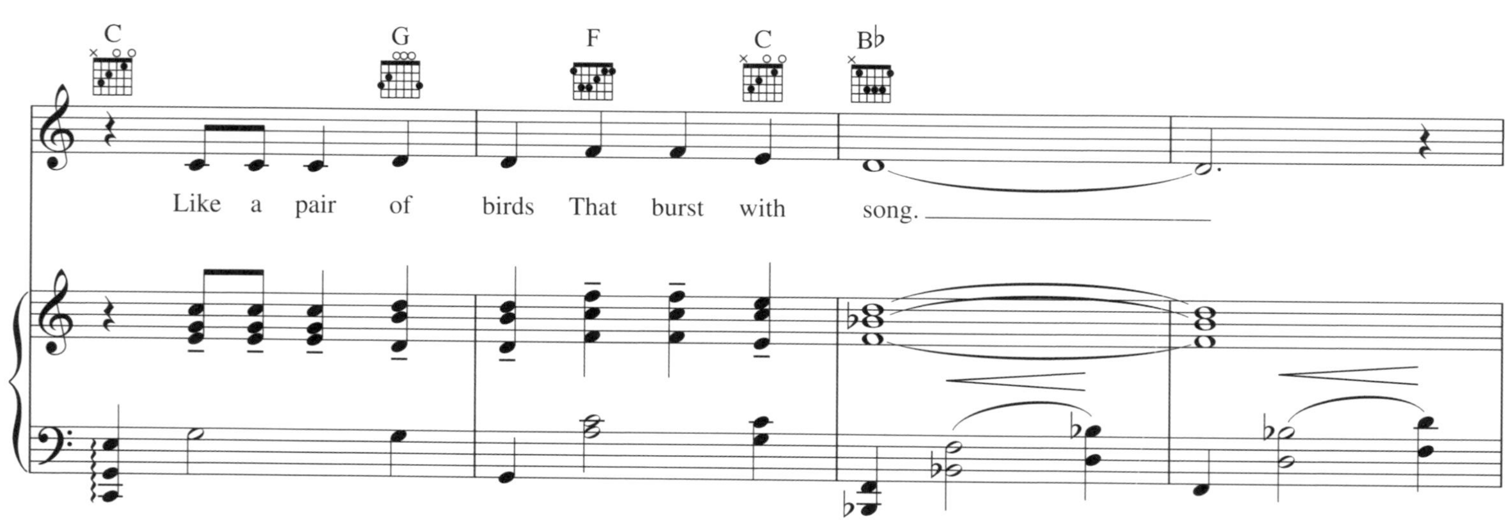

Dm
Gdim
A7♭9
4fr
Dm
Fm6
My eyes look down At your love - ly face
And I hold the
f
C
C♯dim7
Dm7
G7
world
In my em - brace.
mf
molto rit.
Refrain (slowly, with great warmth)
C
G/B
Young - er than Spring - time are you,
Soft - er than star - light
p-mf
C
Am
D
are you,
Warm er than winds of June are the gen - tle lips you

Gmaj7
G7
C
G/B
gave me. Gay-er than laugh-ter are you, Sweet-er than mu-sic
p
C
Am
D
are you, An-gel and lov-er, heav-en and earth are you to
(stay in slow tempo)
G
D7
G
D7
me. And when your youth and joy in-vade my
mf
cresc.
G
D7
G
Dm7
arms And fill my heart as now they do...

G7
C
G
C
G/B
then...
Young-er than Spring-time
am I,
Gay-er than laugh-ter
mp
C
G7/B
C
with passion
Am
am I,
An-gel and lov-er,
heav-en and earth am
cresc.
Am7/D
G7
1
C
G7
I
with
you!
f
allarg.
a tempo
2
C
you!
f dim.
morendo
p

YOU'RE NOBODY 'TIL SOMEBODY LOVES YOU

featured in the Broadway Musical CONTACT

Words and Music by RUSS MORGAN, LARRY STOCK and JAMES CAVANAUGH

Am D7 G6 D7♯5
no - bod - y 'til some - bod - y cares. You
Bm7 B♭dim Am7
may be king, you may pos - sess the world and its gold, but
A6/9 A9♯5 A9 Am7 D7 Am7 D7 D7♯5
5fr 5fr
gold won't bring you hap - pi - ness when you're grow - ing old. The
3
G B7 E7♭9 E7 B7/F♯ E7/G♯
world still is the same, you'll nev - er change it, as

Am
E7
Am
E7/B
sure as the stars shine a - bove.
Am/C
C
C♯dim7
You're no - bod - y 'til some - bod - y loves
G
E7
Am
E7/B
Am/C
A7
D7
you, so find your - self some - bod - y to
R.H.
1
G
F13sus
F9
E♭7sus
E♭7
D9
6fr
4fr
love. You're
2
G
Cm7
3fr
G6
love.
L.H.